D1289666

200 Years of Japanese Porcelain

200 Years of Japanese Porcelain

200 Years of Japanese Porcelain
Introduction and catalogue by Richard S. Cleveland
with an introductory note by John A. Pope

City Art Museum of Saint Louis · Nelson Gallery—Atkins Museum, Kansas City

Copyright 1970 by City Art Museum of Saint Louis
Printed in the United States of America
Library of Congress Catalogue Card Number: 77-141634

Catalogue designed by Richard S. Cleveland;
type set by Warwick Typographers, Inc. in Baskerville
with Torino display face; printed by Sayers Printing
Company on 80 lb. Mountie Velvet for City Art Museum on the
occasion of the exhibition

Exhibition dates:
City Art Museum of Saint Louis October 9–November 15, 1970
Nelson Gallery–Atkins Museum, Kansas City,
December 3, 1970–January 3, 1971

LENDERS TO THE EXHIBITION

FOREWORD

Exhibitions of Japanese porcelain can hardly be said to be frequent occurrences outside of Japan. The most recent and, in fact, the only one to feature these wares exclusively was held fourteen years ago in London under the auspices of the Oriental Ceramic Society, with cooperation from the Arts Council of Great Britain. Now, for the first time in this country, porcelain, as it developed in Japan from the second quarter of the 17th century to the early part of the 19th, is receiving the attention it should command through this exhibition.

When exposed to as large a group of Japanese porcelains as we have the good fortune of studying at first hand in St. Louis and in Kansas City, it may seem curious that they have not been shown more often, if for no other reason than that their beauty of form and decoration makes an immediate appeal to one's aesthetic sensibilities, even though one may not be initiate in the ways of Japanese art. One of the chief reasons for our comparative unfamiliarity with Japanese porcelain is surely that it has not been collected as systematically, nor has it been studied to anything like the same degree, as has the porcelain of China. Much of the Japanese porcelain which made its way to the West in the late 17th and early 18th centuries was in the form of large-scale and sometimes coarsely decorated Imari pieces eminently suited to the ornament of princely interiors. The greatest of these collections was that of Augustus the Strong in his Japanese palace at Dresden which was filled with Chinese and Japanese export wares. It was from these great collections of Imari and Kakiemon that the European perception of Japanese ceramic taste was formed. Although many of the beautiful export wares were appreciated and copied in the West, too often the gaudy and vulgar dominated the taste of Europe. Porcelain of the kind that reflected a purely Japanese aesthetic was seldom encountered in Europe until the beginnings of modern collecting.

In the United States the small group of knowledgeable collectors of the late 19th century who first paid attention to Japanese art overwhelmingly favored pottery over porcelain. For their taste, pottery was—as indeed it was for many Japanese—among the most cultivated forms of artistic expression which Japan had to offer. When porcelain was found in American houses of the period, it was all too often the debased wares which were made in quantity for Western markets and whose most conspicuous representatives were those colossal vases of the kind that John Singer Sargent introduced into his famous portrait of the children of Edward Darley Boit, now in the Museum of Fine Arts, Boston. But no discriminating Japanese would have acknowledged, or much less owned, porcelain objects of this kind. Moreover, if American students of Japanese art had been interested in porcelain, they might not have found it easy to examine for the best wares often remained hidden in private collections.

Following the end of hostilities in 1945, Western, and especially American, interest in Japan increased rapidly and there is today far more public awareness of Japanese art than there has been at any other time. All of her arts are now admired and sought after in the West even though competition from Japanese collectors has limited the opportunities for advantageous buying which were to be found only a short while ago. Yet, Japanese porcelain continues to attract the attention of private collectors and museums in this country and Canada and it is from these collections that we have been privileged to draw important loans for *200 Years of Japanese Porcelain*.

For those who have so generously lent these many beautiful and fragile objects the very least we can do is to note here our most grateful appreciation. While it is customary to say in catalogue *Forewords* that without the cooperation of owners of works of art exhibitions would be impossible to organize, it remains undeniably true that this is so. The two participating museums, therefore, have reason to be indebted to museums and private collectors and also to the many students of Japanese art who, directly or indirectly, contributed to this exhibition. Among museum staff members, certain individuals gave special assistance: Laurence Sickman, director, Nelson Gallery —Atkins Museum, who encouraged the idea of the exhibition from the beginning and who gave helpful advice; Mrs. Clarence Shawgraw, curator, and Miss Yoshiko Kakudo, curator, Center of Asian Art and Culture, The

Avery Brundage Collection; Martin Lerner, assistant curator of Oriental art, The Cleveland Museum of Art; Mark Clark, curator of decorative arts, The Dayton Art Institute, George Kuyayama, senior curator of Far Eastern Art, Los Angeles County Museum of Art; Fong Chow, curator, Far Eastern art, The Metropolitan Museum of Art; Miss Jeanne Harris, associate curator of Oriental art, Nelson Gallery—Atkins Museum; Mrs. Masaaki Ooka, curatorial assistant, Far Eastern art, The Philadelphia Museum of Art; John Vollmer, departmental secretary, Far Eastern Department, Royal Ontario Museum; Miss Bertha Saunders; Henry Trubner, curator of Asiatic art, Seattle Art Museum; Suguru Akutsu, Washington University. Staff members at City Art Museum who have been closely identified with the exhibition are Mrs. James B. Fisher, Jr., research assistant; Mrs. Carl Fox, publications editor; Mrs. Michael Guimbarda, curatorial secretary; Mrs. Herbert M. Patton, registrar; Mrs. Robert C. Rullkoetter, secretary to the director; Stewart Krause and Peter Wilhelm and his staff, who prepared the installation.

The idea for *200 Years of Japanese Porcelain* was proposed by Richard S. Cleveland, the Museum's assistant curator for Oriental art, and in order to know more about the prevalence of these wares in the United States and Canada, he visited public and private collections wherever found. Happily for us, curators and private owners were not only willing to place their valued treasures at our disposal but also to share with Mr. Cleveland their knowledge about individual porcelains which forms the basis for many of his catalogue entries. Mr. Cleveland wrote the accompanying essay and he is also responsible for the design of the catalogue and the tasteful installation of the exhibition.

Finally, it was our particular good fortune to have had Mr. John A. Pope's enthusiastic backing of this exhibition throughout and at every stage to have profited from his profound knowledge in the field of Far Eastern ceramics. Mr. Pope also contributed an enlightening introduction to this catalogue for which I would like to express appreciation on behalf of City Art Museum and the Nelson Gallery—Atkins Museum of Fine Arts.

Charles E. Buckley, *Director*

THE BEGINNINGS OF PORCELAIN IN JAPAN

Even though porcelain was not made in Japan until centuries after it had been in common use in China, the history of its beginnings in the Island Empire has always been obscured in the half-world between legend and history. It was not until the latter part of the 19th century that Western writers began to investigate this history; and from the very beginning the story has been dominated by two legends. The standard books tell us, first, that a certain Gorodaiyu Go Shonzui went to China at the beginning of the 16th century to learn porcelain making from the Chinese. At that time Ming porcelain was flourishing, and our legendary hero could hardly have chosen a better time to learn all the intricacies of the craft. The story goes on to say that he returned to Japan in 1513 bringing with him the necessary materials; that he settled in the province of Hizen where he began, for the first time, to make porcelain in Japan. By this act he automatically became "the father of Japanese porcelain." But, as the story goes, Shonzui's imported materials were soon exhausted; and the manufacture of porcelain ground suddenly to a halt.

At this point we are forced to note that, in respect to this legendary character no single fact or document has come to light to prove that he ever existed. Theories about him vary to such a degree that they bring him back from China in 1513, or in 1520, or again in 1617. Another school of thought identifies him with Takahara Goroshichi, a Chinese (though some say he was a Korean) who had been a protege of the great Toyotomi Hideyoshi who, it will be remembered, launched an all-out assault in the attempt to conquer Korea in 1592, an attempt that came to an end only with his death in 1598. Finally, there is another theory that the name refers to two people: one, Gorodaiyu, a Japanese who went to China where he ordered porcelain made for him; and a second, Go Shonzui, a Japanese reading of the name of the Chinese potter who filled the order.

Professor Tsugio Mikami, John Pope and others at the Tengudani kiln site.

The second legend tells us that a Korean potter named Ri Sampei came back to Japan with a certain Nabeshima Naoshige, a Hizen Daimyo who was a follower of Hideyoshi in the ill-fated campaign of 1592-98. Now this Nabeshima Naoshige was Lord of Saga, a prefecture in the northwestern corner of the island of Kyushu, and he settled Ri Sampei in the village of Taku in the middle of his domain. Lord Naoshige put Ri Sampei to work making pottery and encouraged him in his attempts to make porcelain. The latter venture did not succeed at first, and later on Ri Sampei moved about 12 miles southwest to the town of Tanakamura, the present day Arita. Even there he did not succeed until one day in 1616 when, walking through the hills just east of the town, he discovered a huge deposit of pure porcelain clay in the mountain called Izumiyama. From then on porcelain manufacture became a reality in Japan. The mountain of Izumiyama still stands and, in spite of three and a half centuries of nibbling, continues to yield a seemingly endless supply of the right kind of clay to the thriving porcelain industry of Arita. However, despite the very real existence of the mountain and the thriving industry of Arita, the story of Ri Sampei remained a legend.

Over the years more and more scholars became interested in the history of Arita porcelain; and in 1966, Professor Tsugio Mikami of the Tokyo National University began the scientific excavation of the site of Tengudani which had long been rumored to be the oldest kilnsite in Arita, perhaps founded by the legendary Ri Sampei himself. In 1967, while Professor Mikami's excavations were still in progress, a local amateur whose hobby was the history of Arita porcelain made a most astonishing discovery. This man, Mr. Ikeda Chu-ichi, designer for the Iwao Porcelain Company which manufactures porcelain tiles for all sorts of industrial purposes, was looking through the archives of a small Buddhist temple called Ryusenji in Nishi Arita some five miles west of Arita town. He came upon a document that recorded the death of Ri Sampei. A single line in the temple record is devoted to the death of each member of the parish in chronological order as the death occurred; and the line referring to Ri Sampei gives the following information. It begins with the name GESSO JOSHIN, a Buddhist name given to the deceased after his death. Then comes the expression KAMISHIR-AKAWA SAMPEI; and here his best known name is used when he is called Sampei of Kamishirakawa. This stream (the word Kamishirakawa means

Izumiyama today.

literally "Upper White River") flows through the Valley of the Long-nosed Goblins—which is the English translation of Tengudani, the location then being excavated by Professor Mikami. The rest of the line records the fact that he died on the 11th day of the 8th month of the Meireki era which fell, in our terms, on September 20th, 1655. Unfortunately, the record does not reveal his age at death or we could reconstruct the story even more accurately. If, as the legend has it, he came from Korea an already established potter at the end of the campaign in 1598, he must have lived to a ripe old age. But why not? And, be that as it may, we know at long last that we are dealing with an historical person who lived and flourished in the first half of the 17th century.

So began the history of porcelain in Japan. The finding of the Ryusenji document and the excavation of the Tengudani site, occurring as they did at the same time, provide us with evidence as solid as we may ever expect to find that Ri Sampei was the real discoverer of porcelain clay in Japan and was the first to make porcelain in his kilns at Tengudani. With this start the industry spread rapidly. According to the records more and more Korean potters came over; and the 1637 census lists 800 Korean and Chinese potters in Hizen, 533 of them male and 267 female; and by 1647 there were 555 kilns in the area. Today the number of rediscovered kilnsites may be numbered in the hundreds, and, no doubt, many more lie beneath the villages and towns, especially the sprawling town of Arita itself. Nor was the province of Hizen the only place where this was going on. Within a few decades after the discovery of Izumiyama, and perhaps still within the lifetime of Ri Sampei, a similar discovery was made in the Ishikawa prefecture some 440 miles to the northeast. Here another Korean potter, Goto Saijiro by name, is reported to have discovered a porcelain deposit in a remote and hilly countryside called Kutani (Nine Valleys) and to have begun the manufacture of the porcelain wares that later became world famous under that name. Here again we are in the realm of legend; the true record of Goto Saijiro is still to be found, and the excavation of the Kutani kilnsite has yet to be undertaken.

Much work remains to be done. The history of Japanese porcelain has never stopped, and today the country is one of the great manufacturing centers of the world. To reconstruct the entire history is an immense task; but no part of it is more fascinating than the earliest stage, the stage before 1700. And the emergence of Ri Sampei into the realm of history gives a solid start-

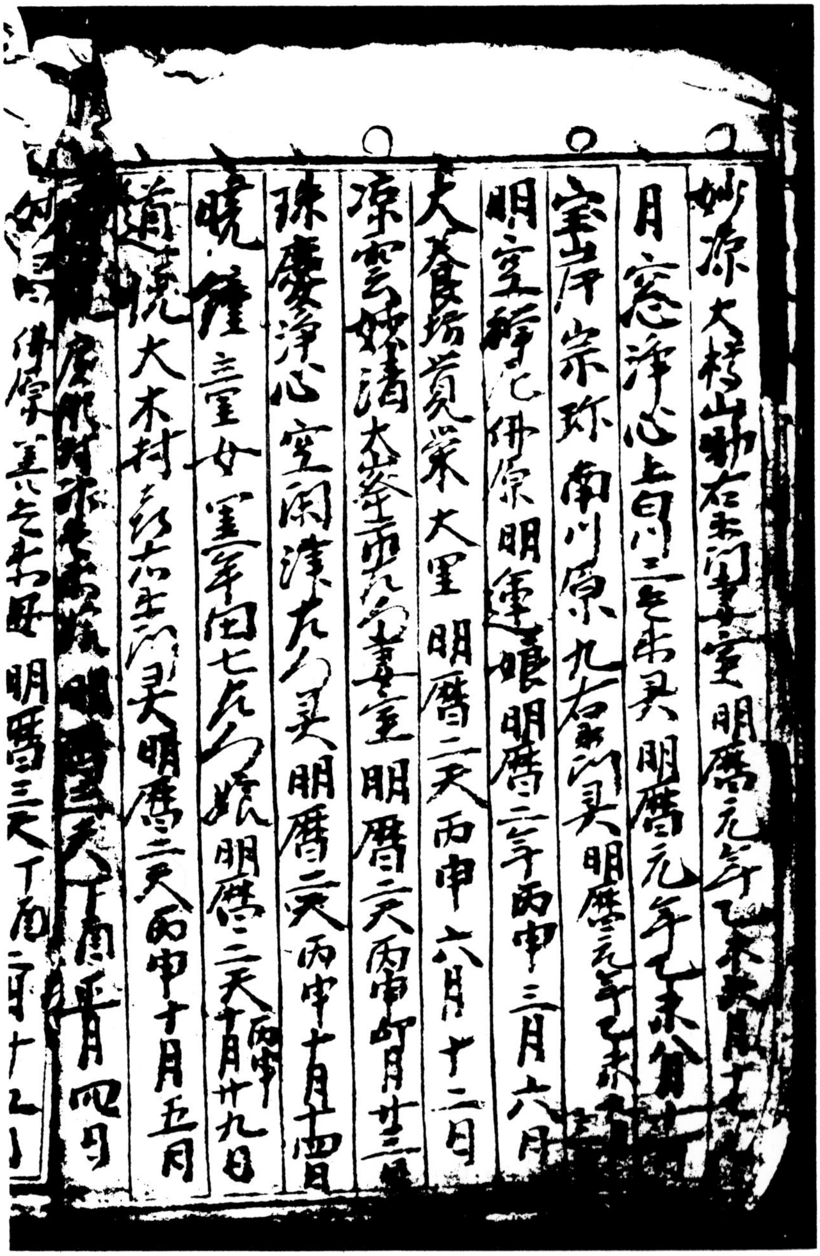

妙原大椿山勤右室閨善室明曆元年乙未朋子

月窓淨心上旬三之朱具朋曆元年乙未分

室序宗珎南川原九右汭具朋曆元年乙未

明室辭乙伊原明運娘明曆二天丙申三月六日

大養房莧棠大里明曆二天丙申六月十二日

凉雲妙清太差王人書室明曆二天丙申帝十月廿三日

珠慶淨心空閑漢夫人明曆二天丙申十月十二日

曉雇三臺女堂辛酉七元娘明曆二天丙申十月廿九日

道曉大木村名空生灵明曆二天丙申十月五日

妙室庠哪不禾吉蕊似川伊原善元书母明曆三天丁酉前月廿二日

ing point such as we have not had before. The problem now is to dig further into the records and further into the ground in the hope of unravelling the rest of the story; and the two places where these efforts must be concentrated are in the prefectures of Saga and Ishikawa. There are lifetimes of work ahead for those who are moved by an unlimited curiosity about the circumstances under which these beautiful things were made.

John A. Pope

Page from the death register in the Ryusenji at Nishi Arita, recording the death of Ri Sampei. Reading from the second line from the right: Gesso Joshin Sampei of Kamishirakawa (became a) spirit on the 11th day of the 8th month of Meireki, the year being *kinoto-hitsuji*—by the modern calendar, September 20th, 1655.

INTRODUCTION

The close of the 16th century saw the return to Japan of the general Toyotomo Hideyoshi from his unsuccessful Korean campaigns of the years 1592-1598. As many soldiers returned landless and impoverished, the homecoming for all too many of them ended with the short sea voyage from Korea to Japan's southernmost large island, Kyushu. This influx of unemployed into a section of the country which was already agriculturally poor was not an insignificant contribution to the increasing development of the island's craft industries and, in particular, to the growing importance of ceramic production. Kyushu had always been influenced by Korea, and in the 16th century numbers of Korean potters settled in the province of Hizen, where they were largely responsible for the establishment of the Karatsu kilns. The new wave of Korean craftsmen brought by Hideyoshi and his lords gave added impetus to the expansion of these and other potteries. The discovery of porcelain clays in 1616 by Li Sampei was propitious for there existed then, besides this discovery, important ingredients for the production of porcelain: the knowledge and skill of the Korean craftsmen along with an available labor force to refine the clays and to provide fuel for the kilns.

The establishment of porcelain production by Li Sampei at Tengudani was soon followed by other kilns, most of which had been producing Karatsu stonewares and which now turned either partially or exclusively to the making of porcelain. These kilns were generally small family operations that used the *noborigama* or stepped hillside kiln to control the drafts and to provide the temperature differentials necessary to firing (see illustration on page 12). These relatively small, family controlled kilns continued until modern times. Japan never developed large factory establishments such as those the Chinese had at Ching Te-chên which, under Imperial control, manufactured wares of superior quality on a mass production basis. One marvels at the technical ability of the Japanese potter who was, in time, to produce wares of exceptionally fine quality using kilns little modified from these essentially primitive types. In spite of the skill of the Koreans, there were problems complicated in the beginning by the necessity of using the natural porcelain clays of Izumiyama rather than mixed clays designed for more suitable firing characteristics. In the case of most forms, a preliminary firing was necessary to "set" the shape. Even so we find, particularly in the case of the large dishes, severe distortion of shape and warpage. The glaze of the early pieces is also often marred by the accretion of foreign matter from the dirty atmosphere of the kiln.

In shape and decoration the early pieces follow most closely the simple almost casual design of the Korean Yi Dynasty wares. Both blue and white and celadon glazed porcelains were made in this fashion but, from the beginning, the Japanese aesthetic along with important influences from the much appreciated Chinese Transitional wares permeated both form and decoration. The shapes were uncomplicated and always utilitarian; tea cups, plates, storage jars, and bottles were the most common vessels produced. Unpretentious landscape designs, floral and plant motives combined with Chinese, Korean and primitive geometric border designs were the earliest decoration. Many of the wares went undecorated, but more often they carried an underglaze blue design even if executed in a most cursory manner. Like the Korean wares to which they are so closely akin, these early pieces frequently display a vitality and strength of design that is both visually pleasing and satisfying in its feel. In the catalogue and in the exhibition these early porcelains are described as "Early Hizen wares," a term often used in Japan which refers to the wares made in the original province of Hizen encompassing the town of Arita and most of the surrounding area where the early wares were fired. The term also serves to distinguish the wares from the more sophisticated porcelains that had begun to appear toward the middle of the 17th century.

Technical proficiency and sophistication of decoration increased with time, encouraged by the flourishing economy and peace of early Edo Japan. Throughout its long history, the Edo period was frought with domestic trouble and natural disasters, but the continuing growth of the economy coupled with the unrelenting expansion of the bourgeoise classes stimulated and continually nourished all the arts. This phenomenon of a culture in dynamic flourescence overseen by a government not only conservative but also reactionary in a land virtually isolated from all foreign intercourse is, in concept, strange to the modern mind. Yet it was this climate of peace and authoritarianism that Japan desperately needed for its economic development and artistic renewal. Fine porcelain is hardly an essential commodity and, for such an industry to flourish, cultural vitality and a society with a surplus of wealth are required. Likewise, economic and cultural vitality are necessary for the development of the production itself. Potters are by the nature of their craft conservative and require stimulation, if not pressure, from outside forces for creative artistic development.

Concurrent with the general cultural flowering of the Early Edo period and aside from the continual demands of the local lords for more and better wares, the most important stimulus for the increase of quality, diversity and production was the presence of the Dutch East India Company and its continual desire for fine trade porcelain. Although in quality the Japanese wares could not at first measure up to the expectations of a European market used to the Chinese *kraak-porselein,* the motivation to improve the fabric and decoration was there. For the Dutch, the troubled state of China after the middle of the 17th century made the China trade increasingly difficult, and the Company was forced to rely more heavily on the porcelain production of the Japanese. The first Western record of the export of Japanese porcelain is in the *Registers* of the Dutch East India Company for the year 1653. Our knowledge of these export wares has come almost exclusively from these records which have been painstakingly researched and published in two volumes by the Dutch scholar, T. Volker, (See refs. 39 and 40). Trade with the Japanese was not easy for the Dutch in spite of their exclusive trading rights with that country since 1639. The Company was used to making outrageous profits based upon high quality, low prices and a dependable supply. The many small Japanese kilns produced porcelain of varying quality; and, as the Dutch were forced to work through middlemen who controlled prices and, in effect, production, a healthy business-like trade situation never really prevailed, even in the heyday of the Japan trade. This situation might have differed had the Dutch been able to treat directly with the porcelain producers, but, after the exclusion decree of 1639, they were forced by the *Bakufu* or the Shogun's central government, to occupy the small artificial island of Deshima in Nagasaki harbor from which they were not permitted to stray, except for a single pilgrimage to Kyoto to make the annual presentation of gifts. Porcelain was but a small part of the trade but one over which the interpreters or middlemen had outstanding control—to the detriment of both the Dutch traders and the porcelain producers. Despite the difficulties encountered, trade continued to flow both in the improved quality blue and white wares after the Chinese style for Europe, and those of rougher quality for the South East Asian and Near Eastern markets. The virtual collapse of the Chinese trade in fine porcelain in the years 1658-82 left the Dutch with exclusive access to fine wares through their relations, however difficult, with the Japanese. In addition to the shapes and decoration by means of models of desired European shapes and patterns of designs in vogue on the Continent (See cat. nos. 32 and 33).

Although the second half of the 17th century saw Japan producing a quantity of wares for export, the home market continued to be served, often with wares identical to those exported or with only slight modification in form or decoration that would better suit the Japanese taste. Around the middle of the 17th century the technique of adding overglaze enamels was learned from the Chinese. The traditional discoverer of the technique was a potter of the Sakaida family in Nangawara who is said to have fashioned an *okimono* or cabinet ornament in the semblance of a pair of persimmons *(kaki)* so delighting the Lord of Nabeshima that he nicknamed Sakaida Kizaiemon, "Kakiemon," a name honorably carried on by his descendents. This charming story is the most popular account of the beginning of the Kakiemon tradition and the beginnings of enameled wares in Japan. Several other versions exist, some more plausible than others, but none are supported by incontrovertible evidence.

Europe was slow to be weaned from its predeliction for blue and white wares, but when it did, it did so with passion. The last quarter of the 17th century saw the development of two distinct styles of overglaze decorated wares: the developed Kakiemon style with its delicate overglaze enamels painted over a sketchy black outline on a fine, white thrown or molded body; and the heavier and more crudely fashioned and decorated Ko-Imari style which utilized a murky underglaze blue overpainted principally with iron reds and gold. Two examples of roughly the same date may be compared in the exhibition in Catalogue numbers 89 and 38. In the latter part of the 17th and in the 18th century both types of wares were exported to the West. The Kakiemon wares, for the most part, retained their refinement and delicacy; the Imari, however, varied greatly, some ruggedly handsome while others were often grotesque in their size, shape and embellishment. While the polychrome ware probably dominated the production, blue and white ware in both the Kakiemon and Imari styles continued to be made for export and domestic use (See cat. nos. 22, 23, 24 and 25).

The terms Kakiemon and Imari can cause confusion as they are commonly applied indiscriminately to wares of varying date and provenance. In origin, the term Kakiemon, of course, comes from the supposed first maker of polychrome wares and his long line of descendents; "Imari" from the small seaport which transshipped the Arita porcelains to Nagasaki for export. The West tends to think of Imari ware as heavily potted and gaudily decorated *nishiki-de* or brocade styled wares exported in the 18th and 19th centuries. In Japan, Imari or Ko-Imari has come to be a catch-all for both early and late wares failing to fall within a specific category such as Kakiemon, Kutani or some other traditionally recognizable type. As such, the term has some merit in its exclusion of other recognizable styles, particularly when qualified by prefixes such as *ko* or old, *kenjo* or gift, and *nishiki-de* or brocade-styled.

If there is some confusion in the terms Imari and Kakiemon, the situation as regards the term Ko-Kutani might be said to be one of chaos. As the state of scholarship, I believe, still stands in this regard, there exists a large group of the most strikingly designed of all Japanese porcelains very tenuously connected by an often obscure aesthetic criteria still hopefully labeled Ko-Kutani. Within the exhibition and the catalogue an effort has been made to sort out the porcelains that either have been, currently are, or would be by some, called Ko-Kutani. Even with as limited a selection as is seen here, the variety is astonishing if not enlightening. (See cat. nos. 50-74). In brief, the most widely accepted Ko-Kutani tradition is as follows: in the mountainous area of Northwestern Japan in Kaga Prefecture, now incorporated into that of Ishikawa, Maeda Toshiyaki, chief of the powerful Maeda clan, established porcelain production at the town of Kutani about the year 1661. Previously, the potter Goto Saijiro had been sent to Arita to learn the secrets of porcelain production and the methods of overglazing in colored enamels. Upon his return, production is said to have begun of a distinctively decorated ware based on designs other than those used at Arita and often associated with the painter Morikage (See cat. no. 50). The production is presumed to have lost its vitality at the end of the 17th and early 18th century and the kilns were eventually closed. In 1816 a certain Yoshidaya Denyemon re-established production at Kutani producing somber hued enameled porcelains in the Ao-Kutani or green Kutani style.

The Ko-Kutani wares are, despite the controversial dating and provenance surrounding them, worthy of the most serious consideration. Their decoration, unlike that of most other porcelains, has an originality of conception and vitality of style that must command the greatest admiration.

The exhibition unfortunately reflects the American situation as regards the collecting of the wares considered to be the earliest of the Ko-Kutani type. Few of these wares are to be seen outside of Japan where they are held in the most reverent esteem. Most of these porcelains, such as the Seattle and Cleveland examples seen in the exhibition (Cat. nos. 53 and 54), are strongly influenced by the Chinese Transitional *Ko-sometsuke* and *Shonzui* wares so beloved by the Japanese tea masters. America has been more fortunate in its collecting of the Ao-Kutani styled wares, whatever their final date and provenance may turn out to be. Some of these pieces were collected in the first quarter of the 20th century, such as the fine piece decorated with lotus designs which was acquired in 1917 by the Indianapolis Institute of Art currently featured in the celebration of the opening of its new museum building. The *Ao-de* or green styled Kutani are best characterized by the complete or nearly complete coverage of the white surface glaze by thick, rich green, blue, aubergine and ocher yellow enamels over a dark, matte brown underdrawing which appears black under the green glaze. Floral and plant designs were favored but other themes are also seen. One of the most striking aspects of the design of these wares is the use of a vibrant, patterned background for the central design and for borders and brims. The backs of the large dishes usually are decorated with rude floral repeats under a sticky turquoise or ocher glaze. Often the base has a *fuku* or *fuku*-like mark within a double square.

After dealing with the intensely troublesome, if superb, Kutani wares, it is more reassuring to treat the wares of the very late 17th and 18th century which, while they also present difficulties, are not so beclouded with myth and contradiction. The Early Edo period ended with the Genroku era (1688-1703). Genroku, however, has a connotation far beyond that of a 15 year period in time. Genroku represents the epitome of stylish grandeur, the creative flowering and dynamic critical response in all areas of life and the arts. Despite sumptuary laws, high prices, and crime in the streets, Genroku was a period and an idea that was not only the fruition of the 17th century but also the hope for the 18th. While theatre, costume, and painting had been highly important to the designs of earlier porcelains, they became even more important in the flourishing climate of Genroku. Building on the successful designs of the 60's and 70's the Kakiemon wares reached what was perhaps the height of their sophistication and taste during this period. During the minority of Kakiemon VI, an uncle, Shibuemon, was given charge of the Kakiemon kilns with the result that a whole new design style was injected into the porcelains of Arita. The exhibition has two examples associated with his name, (See cat. nos. 110 and 112). These examples differ greatly from the usual Kakiemon style, employing both new and old designs, borrowing techniques from the Imari style and, in general, providing a whole new climate and opportunity for innovation. The influence was great but the changes it produced flowered in the wares of Nabeshima more so than in those of Kakiemon.

Although the Nabeshima kiln existed in the latter part of the 17th century, the wares for which it earned its renown were not developed until the early 18th century. Established by the Lord of Nabeshima, the kiln's wares were produced for the exclusive use of the clan from the beginning, and were not sold publicly until the Meiji era. Great secrecy surrounded the production and decoration of the wares to the extent that pieces failing to pass inspection for quality were smashed and buried. Nabeshima ware is best known for the shallow dishes on a high foot decorated with the distinctive and, in the 18th century, exclusive comb pattern (See cat. no. 127). Most of the wares are decorated with highly sophisticated floral and plant motives in an underglaze blue with delicate overglaze enamels. More formal designs are known such as the repeating brocade patterns found on some of the earlier pieces (See cat nos. 117 and 118). Celadon wares were also supposed to have been a most important product of the kiln throughout its long life. Although quality and design suffered from time to time, there seems to have been no period when some fine quality wares were not produced. The wares of Nabeshima, particularly at their height during the Kyoho era, represent better than any other Japanese porcelain the sophistication and style of the Middle Edo period. In addition, they are the last group of early porcelains to be distinguished by a continuum of quality and vitality of design.

Richard S. Cleveland

1. PLATE, Blue and white, Early Hizen ware, Diameter 8¼ inches

Catalogue

2. Deep Dish
Blue and white
Early Hizen ware
Diameter 15½ inches

3. DISH
Blue and white
Early Hizen ware
Diameter 7⅞ inches

4. JAR, Blue and white, Early Hizen ware, Diameter 6½ inches

5. BOTTLE, Blue and white, Early Hizen ware, Height 10 inches

7. LARGE BOTTLE
Celadon
Early Hizen ware
Height 14⅝ inches

6. THREE-FOOTED, FLUTED DISH
Celadon
Early Hizen ware
Diameter 8¾ inches

8. BOTTLE
Celadon
Early Hizen ware
Height 9½ inches

9. SQUARE BOTTLE
Undecorated
Early Hizen ware
Height 7⅞ inches

10. LARGE DISH
Blue and white
Early Hizen ware
Diameter 14 inches

11. BOTTLE
Blue and white
Early Hizen ware
Height 8¾ inches

12. JAR
Blue and white
Early Hizen ware
Height 8⅞ inches

13. WATER CONTAINER
Blue and white
Early Hizen ware
Height 7⅜ inches

14. WINE BOTTLE, Blue and white, Early Hizen ware, Height 12⅝ inches, Underglaze blue

15. PLATE
Blue and white
Early Hizen ware
Diameter 8⅞ inches

16. SMALL JAR
Blue and white
Arita ware
Height 6½ inches

17. EWER WITH BAIL HANDLE
Blue and white
Early Hizen ware
Length 9⅛ inches

18. LARGE BOWL
Blue and white
Arita ware
Diameter 15½ inches

19. DEEP DISH
Blue and white
Arita ware
Diameter 14⅛ inches

20. BOTTLE VASE
Blue and white
Arita ware
Height 9½ inches

21. JAR
Blue and white
Arita ware
Height 10 inches

23. LARGE, LOBED DISH
Blue and white
Arita ware
Diameter 15½ inches

22. LARGE JAR
Blue and white
Arita ware
Height 18½ inches

24. HEXAGONAL JAR
Blue and white
Arita ware
Height 16¼ inches

25. OCTAGONAL JAR
Blue and white
Arita ware
Height 20 inches

26. BOTTLE
Blue and white
Arita ware
Height 11⅞ inches

41

28. DISH WITH EVERTED RIM
Blue and white
Arita ware
Diameter 8½ inches

28. DETAIL OF BACK

29. LARGE PLATE
Blue and white
Arita ware
Diameter 14⅜ inches

30. GOURD-SHAPED BOTTLE
Blue and white
Arita export ware
Height 11⅛ inches

31. JAR
Blue and white
Arita export ware
Height 11¾ inches

44

32. BEER JUG WITH SILVER LID, Blue and white, Arita export ware, Height 10⅝ inches

33. APOTHECARY BOTTLE
Blue and white
Arita export ware
Height 8⅞ inches

33. DETAIL OF BASE

34. V.O.C. Charger
Blue and white
Arita export ware
Diameter 15⅝ inches

35. LARGE PLATE
Blue and white
Arita export ware
Diameter 15 inches

36. LARGE PLATE
Polychrome enamels
Arita export ware
Diameter 14½ inches

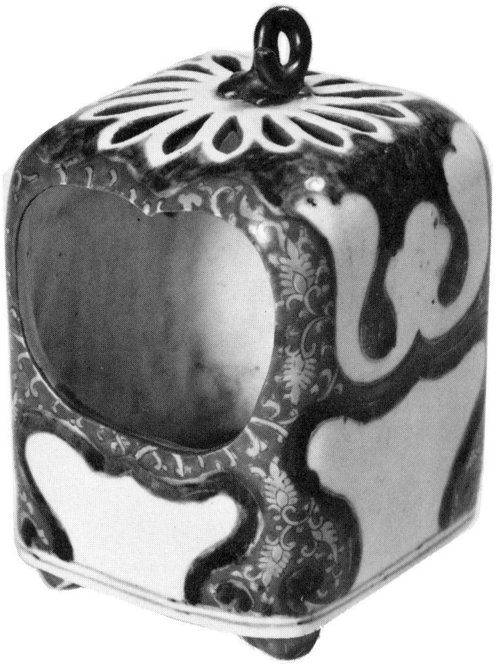

37. HAND WARMER
Underglaze blue and enamels
Ko-Imari style
Height 5⅝ inches

38. PLATE
Underglaze blue and enamels
Ko-Imari style
Diameter 12¼ inches

39. OCTAGONAL JAR, Underglaze blue and enamels, Imari style, Height 16⅛ inches

40. PLATE WITH SCALLOPED RIM
Underglaze blue and enamels
Ko-Imari style
Diameter 12¾ inches

41. WINE BOTTLE
Polychrome enamels
Ko-Imari style
Height 11 inches

42. MODEL OF AN ACTOR
Polychrome enamels
Arita ware
Height 12¼ inches

43. COVERED BOWL
Underglaze blue and enamels
Kenjo Imari style
Diameter 8⅝ inches

44. PLATE
Underglaze blue and enamels
Kenjo Imari style
Diameter 8½ inches

45. BOTTLE
Underglaze blue and enamels
Kenjo Imari style
Height 9¾ inches

46. DEEP BOWL
Underglaze blue and enamels
Kenjo Imari style
Diameter 8⅝ inches

47. TRIANGULAR BOWL
Blue and white
Imari style
Diameter 7⅛ inches

48. Bowl
Underglaze blue and enamels
Ko-Imari style
Diameter 14½ inches

49. DETAIL
Opposite side

49. DETAIL
Base design

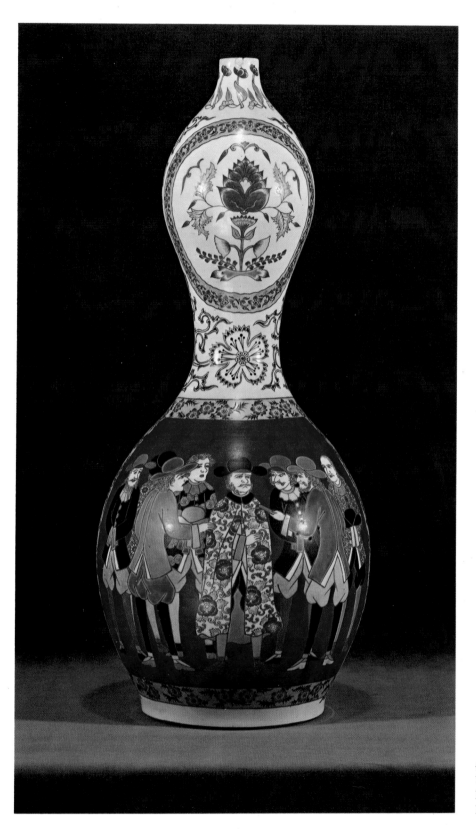

49. Bottle Vase
Underglaze blue and enamels
Imari style
Height 22 inches

50. LARGE DISH
Blue and white
Ko-Kutani style
Diameter 17⅜ inches

52. LARGE BOTTLE
Polychrome enamels
Ko-Kutani style
Height 15¼ inches

51. GOURD-SHAPED BOTTLE
Polychrome enamels
Ko-Kutani style
Height 9¾ inches

53. Dish
Underglaze blue and enamels
Ko-Kutani style
Diameter 12 inches

54. Deep Dish
Underglaze blue and enamels
Ko-Kutani style
Diameter 12⅝ inches

55. DEEP PLATE
Polychrome enamels
Ao-Kutani style
Diameter 14⅞ inches

56. LARGE DISH
Polychrome enamels
Ao-Kutani style
Diameter 14⅜ inches

57. Large Dish
Polychrome enamels
Ao-Kutani style
Diameter 15 inches

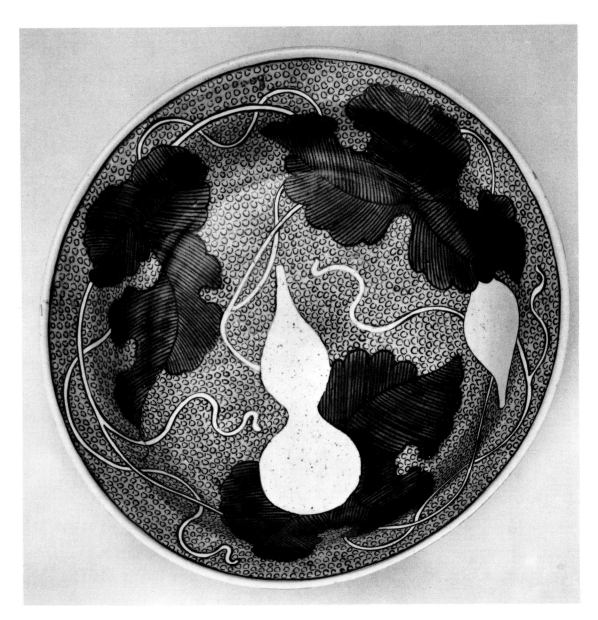

58. DEEP DISH
Polychrome enamels
Ao-Kutani style
Diameter 15⅜ inches

59. LARGE PLATE
Polychrome enamels
Ko-Kutani style
Diameter 16 inches

60. LARGE BOWL, Polychrome enamels, Ao-Kutani style, Diameter 13¼ inches

61. PLATE
Polychrome enamels
Ao-Kutani style
Diameter 8⅜ inches

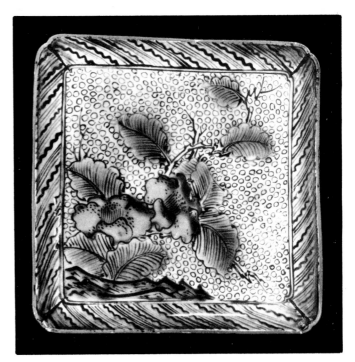

62. SQUARE PLATE
Polychrome enamels
Ao-Kutani style
Width 7 inches

63. LOBED, FOOTED DISH
Polychrome enamels
Ao-Kutani style
Diameter 10 inches

64. DEEP DISH
Polychrome enamels
Ao-Kutani style
Diameter 13⅛ inches

65. Large, Deep Dish
Polychrome enamels
Ao-Kutani style
Diameter 17¾ inches

66. SMALL PLATE
Polychrome enamels
Ko-Kutani style
Diameter 5¾ inches

67. SMALL PLATE
Polychrome enamels
Ko-Kutani style
Diameter 5¾ inches

68. DISH WITH EVERTED RIM, Blue and white, Ko-Kutani style, Diameter 8¼ inches

69. Two Dishes
Blue and white
Arita ware, Ko-Kutani style
Diameter 5¾ inches

70. Dish with Molded Border
Blue and white
Arita ware, Ko-Kutani style
Diameter 8⅜ inches

71. BOTTLE, Blue and white, Arita ware, Imari style, Height 13 inches

72. Jar, Blue and white, Ko-Kutani style, Height 13¼ inches

73. DETAIL OF SIDE PANEL

73. JAR
Polychrome enamels
Ko-Kutani style
Height 11¾ inches

74. JAR, Polychrome enamels, Ko-Kutani style, Height 11½ inches

75. SMALL PLATE
Overglaze blue
Suisaka ware
Diameter 5⅛ inches

76. SMALL PLATE
Blue and white
Suisaka ware
Diameter 5⅞ inches

77. JAR
Polychrome enamels
Early Kakiemon style
Height 8⅝ inches

78. KENDI, Polychrome enamels, Early Kakiemon style, Height 8⅞ inches

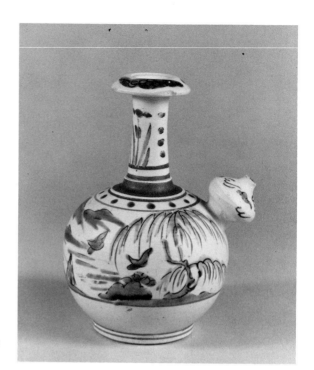

79. KENDI
Polychrome enamels
Early Kakiemon style
Height 6¼ inches

79. DETAIL
Opposite side

80. Jar, Polychrome enamels, Early Kakiemon style, Height 11 inches

81. BOTTLE
Polychrome enamels
Kakiemon style
Height 11 inches

82. JAR, Polychrome enamels, Early Kakiemon style, Height 7¾ inches

83. DETAIL OF BACK

83. MODEL OF A BEAUTY, Polychrome enamels, Kakiemon style, Height 15 inches

84. TEAPOT
Polychrome enamels
Kakiemon style
Height 6⅜ inches

85. WINE EWER
Polychrome enamels
Kakiemon style
Width 7½ inches

86. JUG OR EWER, Polychrome enamels, Kakiemon style, Height 8½ inches

87. DISH
Polychrome enamels
Kakiemon style
Diameter 12½ inches

88. LARGE DISH
Polychrome enamels
Kakiemon style
Diameter 12⅜ inches

89. BOTTLE
Polychrome enamels
Kakiemon style
Height 15¾ inches
[Cover illustration]

90. OCTAGONAL BOWL
Polychrome enamels
Kakiemon style
Diameter 10 inches

91. Large Bowl
Polychrome enamels
Kakiemon style
Diameter 13 inches

92. COVERED BOWL
Polychrome enamels
Kakiemon style
Diameter 8¼ inches

95. OCTAGONAL BOWL
Undecorated
Kakiemon style
Diameter 8⅜ inches

93. OCTAGONAL BOWL
Polychrome enamels
Kakiemon style
Diameter 8 inches

94. OCTAGONAL BOWL
Polychrome enamels
Kakiemon style
Diameter 7½ inches

96. DISH IN CHRYSANTHEMUM SHAPE
Polychrome enamels
Kakiemon style
Diameter 6 inches

97. CHRYSANTHEMUM-SHAPED BOWL, Polychrome enamels, Kakiemon style, Diameter 7⅜ inches

98. VASE, Polychrome enamels, Kakiemon style, Height 10½ inches

99. DEEP BOWL
Polychrome enamels
Kakiemon style
Diameter 13½ inches

110

100. CHRYSANTHEMUM-SHAPED BOWL
Polychrome enamels
Kakiemon style
Diameter 8½ inches

101. Lobed Dish
Polychrome enamels
Kakiemon style
Diameter 7 inches

112

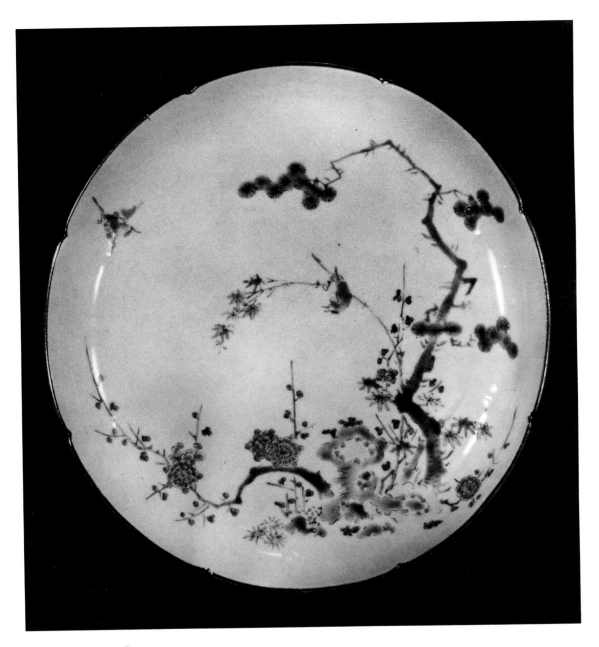

102. EIGHT-LOBED PLATE
Polychrome enamels
Kakiemon style
Diameter 7⅜ inches

103. EIGHT-LOBED DISH
Polychrome enamels
Kakiemon style
Diameter 8½ inches

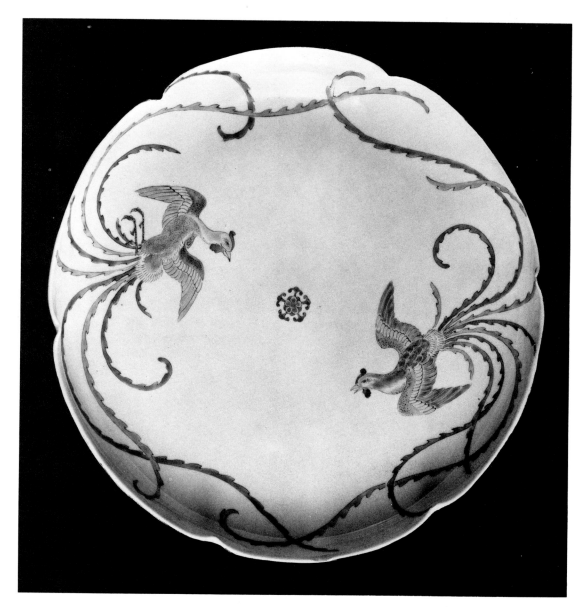

104. Six-Lobed Bowl
Polychrome enamels
Kakiemon style
Diameter 9¾ inches

105. SQUARE BOTTLE, Polychrome enamels, Kakiemon style, Height 8⅞ inches

106. LOBED BOWL
Polychrome enamels
Kakiemon style
Diameter 10 inches

108. Dish with Peony Design
Polychrome enamels
Arita ware
Diameter 7¼ inches

109. PAIR OF BOWLS
Polychrome enamels
Kakiemon style
Diameter 8 inches

110. DEEP DISH
Underglaze blue and enamels
Kakiemon style
Diameter 8⅛ inches

111. LOBED PLATE
Blue and white
Kakiemon style.
Diameter 8½ inches

112. DETAIL OF BACK

122

112. LARGE, LOBED PLATE
Polychrome enamels
Shibuemon style
Diameter 13½ inches

113. PLATE, Blue and white, Kakiemon style, Diameter 8¼ inches

114. PLATE
Blue and white
Kakiemon style
Diameter 8¾ inches

115. FOOTED DISH
Underglaze blue and enamels
Nabeshima ware
Diameter 6 inches

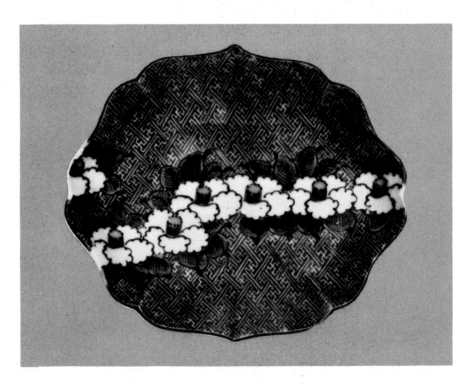

116. MOLDED DISH, Underglaze blue and enamels, Nabeshima ware, Length 6 inches

117. Footed Dish
Underglaze blue and enamels
Nabeshima ware
Diameter 6⅛ inches

118. Footed Dish
Underglaze blue and enamels
Nabeshima ware
Diameter 5⅞ inches

119. CUP WITH SILVER LINER
Underglaze blue and enamels
Nabeshima ware
Diameter 3½ inches

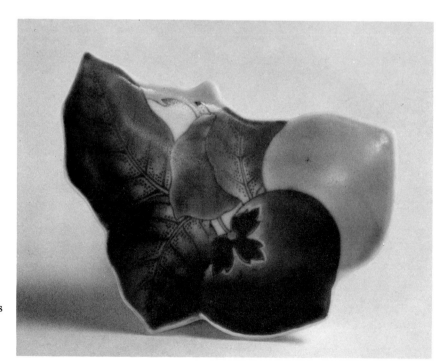

120. SET OF FIVE MOLDED DISHES
Underglaze blue and enamels
Nabeshima ware
Diameter 4 inches

121. FOOTED DISH, Underglaze blue and enamels, Nabeshima ware, Diameter 6 inches

123. FOOTED DISH
Underglaze blue and enamels
Nabeshima ware
Diameter 5⅞ inches

122. FOOTED DISH
Underglaze blue and enamels
Nabeshima ware
Diameter 5⅞ inches

124. FOOTED DISH
Underglaze blue and enamels
Nabeshima ware
Diameter 5⅞ inches

125. TWO SMALL, FOOTED DISHES
Underglaze blue and enamels
Nabeshima ware
Diameter 5¾ inches

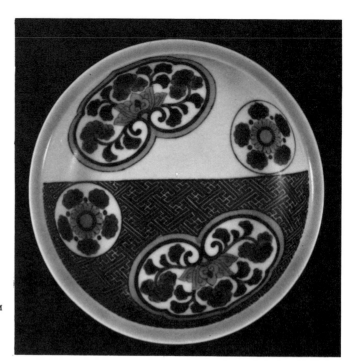

126. DISH WITH CELADON RIM
Blue and white
Nabeshima ware
Diameter 6 inches

127. FOOTED DISH, Underglaze blue and enamels, Nabeshima ware, Diameter 8⅛ inches

128. FOOTED DISH
Underglaze blue and enamels
Nabeshima ware
Diameter 8 inches

129. FOOTED DISH
Underglaze blue and enamels
Nabeshima ware
Diameter 4½ inches

130. FOOTED DISH
Underglaze blue and celadon
Nabeshima ware
Diameter 8 inches

131. DISH
Underglaze blue and celadon
Nabeshima ware
Diameter 7⅞ inches

132. FOOTED DISH
Underglaze blue
Nabeshima ware
Diameter 8 inches

133. FOOTED DISH
Underglaze blue
Nabeshima ware
Diameter 12 inches

134. FOLIATED DISH
Blue and white
Arita ware, Matsugatani style
Length 6⅝ inches

135. SMALL FOLIATE DISH
Underglaze blue and enamels
Arita ware, Matsugatani style
Length 6⅜ inches

136. COVERED JAR
Blue and white
Hirado ware
Height 8½ inches

Notes to the Catalogue

ERAS IN THE EDO PERIOD

EARLY EDO

Genwa	1615-1623
Kanei	1624-1643
Shoho	1644-1647
Keian	1648-1651
Shoo	1652-1654
Meireki	1655-1657
Manji	1658-1660
Kambun	1661-1672
Empo	1673-1680
Tenwa	1681-1683
Jokyo	1684-1687
Genroku	1688-1703

MIDDLE EDO

Hoei	1704-1710
Shotoku	1711-1715
Kyoho	1716-1735
Gembun	1736-1740
Kampo	1741-1743
Enkyo	1744-1747
Kanen	1748-1750
Horeki	1751-1763
Meiwa	1764-1771
Anei	1772-1780
Temmei	1781-1788
Kansei	1789-1800

LATE EDO

Kyowa	1801-1803
Bunka	1804-1817
Bunsei	1818-1829
Tempo	1830-1843
Koka	1844-1847
Kaei	1848-1853
Ansei	1854-1859
Manen	1860
Bunkyu	1861-1863
Genji	1864
Keio	1865-1867

1

PLATE

Landscape design in underglaze blue
Early Hizen ware
Genwa-Kanei eras, 1615-1643
Diameter: 21.0 cm. Height: 3.2 cm. Foot: 7.5 cm.
The University of Michigan Museum of Art,
James Marshall Plummer Memorial Collection,
Gift of Mr. Harry Packard
1963/2.62

Chinese landscape themes were among the first motives used on early Hizen porcelain. Although the compositions vary, the basic elements of fantastic cliffs, houses, boats, island and moon almost invariably appear. In addition, scholars in landscapes or seen in retreat in mountain pavilions are often present, as in the Seattle teapot (cat. no. 17). Other elements such as the great old fir trees seen in Mrs. Bunting's plate (cat. no. 2), appear frequently. Late Ming painting is presumably the direct or indirect source of these designs. The probability of any Korean influence in such exotic and fabulous landscapes seems remote. It is interesting to note in this particular dish that despite the crude simplicity of the potting and decoration, the composition retains the essential spacial relationships of a comparable landscape painting mounted on a *kakimono*. The competence of the designers of early porcelain can hardly be laid to chance or intuition for, in this and so many other examples, what appears as artless craftsmanship is underlayed by a viable aesthetic intent.

2

DEEP DISH

Landscape design in underglaze blue
Early Hizen Ware
Genwa-Kanei eras, 1615-1643
Diameter: 39.4 cm. Height: 9.5 cm. Foot: 16.7 cm.
Nelson Gallery—Atkins Museum,
Gift of Mrs. George H. Bunting, Jr.
69.34/2

Large early dishes such as this are usually attributed to the Kuromuta kiln. They are characterized by exotic Chinese landscapes in the central portion of the interior, and simple geometric or formalized motives repeated on the relatively wide, sloping brim. This particularly fine example is decorated with the vigorous design of a grotesquely gnarled old pine tree growing from outcroppings of rock rising above water. A ringed moon rides above two craggy mountain peaks jutting through the mists while formalized cloud forms are seen scudding through space at the top of the composition. The fantastic landscape is contained by double blue lines and a repeating lotus pattern. The upper portion of the dish is almost flat, as is the brim, which is decorated with a simple geometric floral repeat between blue lines. The rim is finished with a moderately heavy, rounded beading. The dish is well and heavily potted of fine clean clay. It was, however, badly warped in the firing. The glaze is of irregular thickness due most probably to the firing difficulties and warping. The footring is small in relation to the dish's size, and is burned pink at the edges. The almost flat, glazed bottom shows one spur mark in the center. The underglaze painting is quick but sure in the development of the motive line and substance of the shading. The color runs from a dark, blue-black to a greyed pale blue. These substantially formed early wares are to be appreciated for the rugged, sensible quality of their potting and the charm and vigor of their painting. The warped and cracked bodies, and the uneven, pitted, crackled glaze that are anathema to the connoisseur of late Chinese porcelain mean little here. For comparable pieces, see the Oakland Catalogue (See ref. 15, nos. 83 and 84, pls. 44 and 45).

3

DISH

Pine tree motif in underglaze blue
Arita ware, Imari type
Keian period, 1648-1651
Diameter: 20.0 cm. Height: 4.5 cm. Foot: 7.8 cm.
Philadelphia Museum of Art,
Gift of Theodore T. Newbold
66-119-1

This interesting dish is dated to the Keian period by the Philadelphia Museum. While such a dating would seem rather narrow in span, it is reasonable in that it is indicative of the transitional aspects of the dish between the Early Hizen style and that of the developed Imari style. The size, flat brim, small foot and thick potting would lead one naturally to the Heikoba kiln of the late 1630's or early forties as the origin of the piece; however, the appearance of the glaze, the decoration of the brim, the quality of the blue as well as the handling of the design all tend to place it just a bit later. Although far from being a masterpiece of early porcelain, this small dish has a charm and naivete about it that make it very pleasing. The design of the old pine is simple, straight-forward and interesting. The running scroll around the brim frames the composition well and gives some motive power to the design. The "poem" written in careless *kanji* to the right of the pine means nothing. Either through plan or inspiration the decorator was compelled to place a line of characters to the right of the pine for balance and content. He did this using characters readily found about the kiln on bundles, barrels and orders. Many of the characters are ciphers used in trade for numbers which in Japanese notation are simply constructed and easily "raised." It requires but one stroke to make a one into a ten, which is even simpler than the addition of a zero in our Arabic notation. The dish is well and strongly potted with a fairly thick glaze which runs quite greenish-blue where thick. The glaze is quite clean and the underglaze blue, while greyed, is clear and rich. The short foot has an accumulation of kiln grit on the inside.

4

JAR

Decoration of pine and plum in underglaze blue
Early Hizen ware
Genwa-Kanei eras, 1615-1643
Height: 21.4 cm. Diameter: 16.5 cm. Foot: 9.5 cm.
Center of Asian Art and Culture,
The Avery Brundage Collection,
M. H. de Young Memorial Museum
B64 P28

This jar, although nearly identical in size to the Michigan example (cat. no. 12), is signif-

icantly different in design, particularly in the form itself. It is more ovoid in shape, having almost no shoulder. There is an observable foot to the pot and, most significant of all, the high collar-like neck is unmistakably of Korean rather than Japanese design. The slightly splayed foot is also more in the Korean than in the Japanese tradition. Like the Michigan jar, the design is placed on the upper portion of the body: however, in this case, it is more rigidly contained in the upper two-thirds by a double blue line. While the painting of both jars is similar in technique, the Brundage jar's painting is softer in appearance and lighter in tone because of the slight contrast in the tonality of the underglaze blue. In addition, the design is more simply conceived. The broad neck of the jar is handsomely decorated by a band of overlapping chrysanthemums between double lines. The glaze on the Brundage piece is a bit thinner and tends to be somewhat more irregular in the coverage of the body. It is considerably cleaner than the Michigan piece, although it does show the pocking and pitting common among these early wares.

5

BOTTLE

Floral and net design in underglaze blue
Early Hizen ware
Genwa-Kanei eras, 1615-1643
Height: 25.4 cm. Diameter: 11.4 cm. Foot: 6.9 cm.
Center of Asian Art and Culture,
The Avery Brundage Collection,
M. H. de Young Memorial Museum
B66 P17

The simple elegance of this common shape is enhanced by the ingenuity of the designer. The essentially geometric quality of the often-used design, the fishnet, here is abstracted into a freely drawn descending triangular shape separating the body of the vessel into three broad areas which emphasize the circular motives between those same net designs on the shoulder. Miss Kakudo of the Brundage Collection suggests that these medallions represent a view of an opened morning glory. Various other suggestions as to the meaning of the design have been offered, but this one seems to be the most sensible. The morning glory flower, leaves and vine were often used in the designs of early pottery and porcelain in Kyushu but a more telling argument lies in simply looking straight into a morning glory bloom. Even the manner in which the net design hooks about the horizontal encircling line on the body is reminiscent of the vine tendril. Discovery of content or reading a great deal into these simple designs is hardly necessary for their appreciation, but it is worthwhile to consider the often substantial aesthetic at the root of the designs. Whether the design itself originated in China, Korea or Japan, most of the wares, such as this bottle, were decorated to the taste of the Japanese. This bottle is recorded as being a probable product of the Tengudani kiln. See Jenyns, pl. 1A in ref. 14, and *Ko Imari,* ref. 30, fig. 18, p. 310.

6
THREE-FOOTED, FLUTED DISH
Incised design under a celadon glaze, brown rim.
Early Hizen ware
Genwa-Kanei eras, 1615-1643
Diameter: 22.3 cm. Height: 5.0 cm.
Center of Asian Art and Culture,
The Avery Brundage Collection,
M. H. de Young Memorial Museum
B64 P32

Although scalloped or fluted bowls are quite common to both Chinese and Korean pottery and porcelain, their form usually is described as lotiform. The veneration of the chrysanthemum in Japan naturally led Japanese potters to adapt the scalloped or lotiformed shape into forms close to the *kiku-mon,* or chrysanthemum crest, form. This dish with its incised design of overlapping lotus leaves in the center is clearly derived from Korean models, but the regular multi-lobed fluting shows a tendency away from the lotus form and perhaps toward that of the *kiku.* The ultimate refinement of the fluted bowl in chrysanthemum shapes comes in the late

17th century Kakiemon wares (See cat. no. 97). The dish rests on three feet shaped in the form of animal paws evenly placed about an unglazed footring. The central portion of the bottom is glazed. The dish is heavily potted of fine clay, the glaze is quite thick and bubbly and, though similar to the other celadon pieces in the exhibition, it is darker green in appearance. Whether the unglazed footring is just a convention or was necessary in the firing of a footed piece such as this is uncertain (See ref. 15, pl. 59b for an Early Hizen celadon bowl which also displays a brown rim).

7
LARGE BOTTLE
Incised decoration under a celadon glaze
Early Hizen Ware
Genwa-Kanei eras, 1615-1643
Height: 37.0 cm. Diameter: 20.0 cm. Foot: 13.0 cm.
Private Collection

Many early Hizen kilns produced celadon glazed wares. When this bottle was exhibited in Oakland, the catalogue entry noted that celadon shards had been discovered at the Heikoba and Hyakken kiln sites. Collections of shards from other early sites also indicate that celadon wares were a common production of the early kilns. The glaze itself is the primary decoration of the vessel. Even the incised patterning around the body derives its effect not so much from its hatched patterns as from the effect produced by the thick glaze in the incisions. The pale blue-green glaze is exceptionally beautiful in appearance. It is very thick and has a bubble structure which would probably best be described as frothy—the effect of which is an appearance of exceptional depth through the reflection and refraction of light within the structure of the glaze. The bottom of the short, almost straight foot is unglazed, burned pink in the firing, and bears some accretion of grit from the kiln.

PUBLISHED: Koyama, Fujio (ed.). *Japanese Ceramics From Ancient to Modern Times.* Oakland: Oakland Art Museum, 1961, no. 99, pl. 58.
FORMER COLLECTION: Nathan Hammer

8

BOTTLE
Incised decoration under a celadon glaze
Early Hizen ware
Genwa-Kanei eras, 1615-1643
Height: 24.1 cm. Diameter: 12.7 cm. Foot: 8.2 cm.
Center of Asian Art and Culture,
The Avery Brundage Collection,
M. H. de Young Memorial Museum
B64 P36

It is perhaps of interest to compare this bottle with the other Early Hizen bottles in the exhibition. While the forms of the Brundage (cat. no. 5) and Stanford (cat. no. 11) examples are similar in the absence of a visible foot, the general shape, particularly the mouth of the Brundage bottle, bears a closer resemblance to the large celadon bottle (cat. no. 7). Both of the celadon bottles have vertical incised patterning around the body and observable potting chatter around the neck. The similarities and differences among the three bottles point up the difficulties encountered in assigning these early wares to a specific kiln. This small wine bottle has the same characteristics as the large celadon vessel in terms of the quality of the celadon glaze though, of course, it is proportionately thinner. Although the neck is of about the same diameter as that of the Stanford bottle, it appears much thinner because of the upward sweeping line and the width of the elegant trumpet mouth.

9

SQUARE BOTTLE
Early Hizen Ware
Genwa-Kanei eras, 1615-1643
Height: 20.0 cm. Width: 9.6 cm. Foot: 7.0 cm.
Private Collection

The shape of this small but solidly formed vessel is of Korean derivation. It appears to have been produced through a combination of coil method and wheel potting, the latter used for the final building and finishing. If such is the case, it would have much in common with Karatsu stonewares and particularly those in the Chosen-Karatsu tradition. Many of the Karatsu kilns gave way to porcelain manufacture early in the 17th century and many continued making both Karatsu ware and porcelain at the same site (See ref. 15, p. 35, and ref. 14, p. 101). This handsome small piece is heavily potted in a sturdy shape but one which is not without grace. The sides swell outward slightly to a pleasingly rounded, high shoulder. The two rounded rings that support the gently flaring neck repeat in a smaller scale the curves of the shoulder and form a strong support for the neck. The glaze is thick, uneven and shows accretions from the kiln during firing as well as pocking and other irregularities.

10

LARGE DISH
Floral and bird design in underglaze blue
Early Hizen ware
2nd quarter 17th century
Diameter: 35.5 cm. Height: 9.0 cm. Foot: 10.0 cm.
Private Collection

There are both Chinese and Korean precedents for the petal form and impressed radial elements which characterize this large and handsome dish. While the piece is somewhat crudely fashioned and poorly finished on the exterior, the potting is remarkably light for a dish of its size. The relatively small foot rim is short, square in section and slopes inward slightly. The lively painting of the hawk-like bird and oversized floral landscape is contained within double blue lines in the central medallion. The design is painted in a greyed blue shading from the palest wash to a very dark bluish-black. Both in potting and painting there is a rugged vitality that is very satisfying to the hand and the eye.

PUBLISHED: Old Imari Research Committee (ed). *Old Imari.* Tokyo: Saga: Kinkado, 1959, pl. 29.

11

BOTTLE
Plum and pine in underglaze blue
Early Hizen ware
Genwa-Kanei eras, 1615-1643
Height: 22.2 cm. Diameter: 12.0 cm. Foot: 7.2 cm.
Stanford University Museum
65.64

The solid and direct form of this bottle is simply decorated with designs of plum branches with pine branches on the opposite side. The sure drawing in an impure underglaze blue pigment is unpretentious but very harmoniously fitted to the vessel's form. Both form and painting reflect a Korean influence or hand. This bottle is probably from the Tengudani kiln site area.

12

JAR
Pine, plum and bamboo in underglaze blue
Early Hizen ware
Genwa-Kanei eras, 1615-1643
Height: 21.6 cm. Diameter: 11.5 cm. Foot: 10.2 cm.
The University of Michigan Museum of Art,
Margaret Watson Parker Art Collection
1964/1.99

Simple, useful storage jars of this shape were made all over the Far East from the earliest times. We may look for the more direct prototype of this particular form in the Kamakura period wares, particularly those of the old Seto and Tamba types. The jar is potted to a form that is both attractive and functional, with a short, sloping neck with everted lip, simply swelling body, and relatively wide foot. The foot and neck diameters are just about equal. Three round lungs have been applied to the shoulder. These, along with the formation of the neck and lip, would serve for the attachment of a cover. This jar would not have had a porcelain cover, but rather one of organic materials possibly with straw cord ties. The upper three-quarters of the jar is decorated with three approximately equally sized renderings of the traditional "three friends"

design of pine, plum and bamboo. These designs are hastily but competently drawn in a greyed underglaze blue that runs dark blue-black where thick. The neck is decorated with opposing floral and leafy scrolling motives between double blue lines. The thick glaze is pocked and shows flecks of foreign matter acquired in the firing.

PUBLISHED: "College Museum Notes, Acquisitions," *Art Journal,* Vol. XXIV, No. 1 (Fall, 1964), p. 52.

13

WATER CONTAINER
Floral design in underglaze blue
Early Hizen ware
Genwa-Kanei eras, 1615-1643
Height: 19.3 cm. Diameter: 19.3 cm. Foot: 9.8 cm.
Private Collection

Early porcelain tea ceremony pieces of quality are hardly common in Japan and quite rare in American collections. This large and highly important *mizusashi* is an unusually fine example of its type. Its size alone gives it presence. The squat, tapering, drum-like lower body is balanced on a relatively small footring; a fairly sharp angle produces a secondary shoulder on this lower body which continues almost vertically upward into a soft curve that culminates in a short and almost vertical neckring. The whole is sturdy, harmonious and pleasing in its truncated ovoid form. The wide band of chrysanthemum flowers with their airy, leafy scrolling is lightly contained between double blue lines. The spacious composition of the design combined with the immediacy of the drawing enhances the strong shape rather than merely decorating, much less dominating, it. Between double lines at the top of the jar a repeat of floral or cloud forms surmounted by a triangulated dentil design of dark blue accentuates the curve and angle of the topmost shoulder. A lacquered wood cover seen in the illustration is not contemporary with the piece.

14

WINE BOTTLE
Molded form with underglaze blue decoration
Early Hizen ware
Genwa-Kanei eras, 1615-1643
Height: 32.1 cm.
Mr. and Mrs. James Martin

The form of this bottle probably has its roots in the Korean tradition where ceramics were fashioned in vegetal forms from the Early Koryo period. The squash-like form of this bottle is decorated with floral and plant motives in alternate panels separated by single and double vertical raised moldings. A double band of *sei-gai-ha,* or wave pattern, surrounds the bottom of the neck of the vessel and provides an arched finish to the top of the panels on the body. The underglaze blue decoration is painted with vigor but has an overall quality of delicacy. This decoration fills the panels, giving emphasis to the undecorated panels and, thereby, making the handsome form of the vessel more apparent. Other bottles of this form are known in Japan and shards have been found at the sight of the Hyakken kiln (See ref. 30, p. 76, text pl. 74).

15

PLATE
Floral decoration in underglaze blue
Early Hizen Ware
Genwa-Kanei eras, 1615-1643
Diameter: 22.6 cm. Height: 3.2 cm. Foot: 9.5 cm.
Eugene Fuller Memorial Collection,
Seattle Art Museum
62.J26.27

The subtle three dimensional quality which is so readily apparent on actually seeing this plate is not well translated by the camera. The floral forms with their highly stylized drawing of leaves and tendrils are patterned in a strong curve that moves from the top left of the plate, then sweeps around to almost close the circular pattern at the top. Through this opening, a recurving of five butterflies moves toward the center of the composition. The effect of this delightful design is one of butterflies appearing to swarm into the field of flowers. The whole design is neatly contained by the augmented lotus repeat design on the brim. The plate is painted in dark tones ranging from a greyed blue to a dark blue shade which is almost black. Although quite thickly potted in the center, the outside edges are relatively thin with a narrow, flat and slightly sloping brim finished with a rounded beading. A sharp curve separates the brim from the interior of the plate which is quite flat. The foot is very short and is square in section.

16

SMALL JAR
Peony and orchid leaves in underglaze blue
Arita ware, second half 17th century
Height: 16.5 cm. Diameter: 12.6 cm. Foot: 8.1 cm.
Center of Asian Art and Culture,
The Avery Brundage Collection,
M. H. de Young Memorial Museum
B62 P27

The Ming Transitional lidded jars of ovoid shape seen in 17th century Dutch painting seem to be the direct antecedent of this fine vessel. Both shape and decoration have been modified to the Japanese taste. The falling blade design so often seen on the Ming prototypes is here simplified into a simple chevron repeat on the shoulder. In addition, the design and rendering of the peony and orchid motif have a very definite Japanese feeling akin in many respects to those blue and white wares labeled either Kutani or Kutani style. The comb pattern at the neck may also be related to Ming porcelain, but it is more likely that it was a design already in favor which had come into use through imported *Ko-sometsuke* or *Shonzui* wares. In both shape and design the jar shows a simple elegance which is in many respects superior to most of the Chinese export wares from which it is derived. The painting is sure and handsomely fitted to the surface. The underglaze blue is of good color and the glaze is reasonably clean and quite white.

17

EWER WITH BAIL HANDLE
Decorated in underglaze blue
Early Hizen ware
Genwa-Kanei eras, 1615-1643
Length: 22.9 cm. Height: 22.4 cm. Foot: 12.2 cm.
Seattle Art Museum
70.J26.32

The sturdy form of this wine pot is distinguished by the handsomely decorated oval reserve panels of Chinese landscapes. The side illustrated here depicts a moonlight scene of scholars in a pavilion on a lake in winter from which two figures are departing in the snow. The reverse side shows two figures on a bridge in a landscape. Both scenes are skillfully executed in a rich dark blue-black underglaze color, as are the decorative elements on the rest of the vessel. The dense scrolling and predominantly dark annular band at the top are excellent foils for the openness of the composition of the landscapes with their dark, decisive lines and dramatic forms in dark silhouette. The arching handle, besides its obvious usefulness, adds a significant degree of lightness to the otherwise squat, heavy form of the pot by carrying the curved lines of the reserves and the form into a pleasantly ovoid profile. The lower portion of the ewer is potted in much the same manner as a bottle. A clean, thick glaze runs blue-green and very bubbly around the handles, spout and top of the foot. This handsome ewer probably came from the Hyakken or related kiln.

18

LARGE BOWL
Heron design in underglaze blue
Arita ware, Ko-Imari type
Second half 17th century
Diameter: 39.5 cm. Height: 8.1 cm. Foot: 17.7 cm.
City Art Museum of Saint Louis,
W. K. Bixby Oriental Art Trust Fund
342:62

This very large and showy specimen of Early Imari style is very much in the Japanese taste.

Although a number of foreign influences or motives may be determined in the piece, i.e. the banana tree of Transitional Ming blue and white or the very K'ang Hsi type of butterfly, the working out of the design is very much in the Japanese manner. The two herons are painted with some wit standing in water in which reeds and lotus are seen. This scene is contained between double lines and the surrounding border is quite broad—about half the width of the center reserve—and carries its own landscape theme of water, rocks and banana trees along with the arbitrary inclusion of the large butterfly. The design is freely and rapidly drawn in fairly rich blue. Washes in lighter and darker greyed blue are layed over solid areas. Some of the drawing is done with light wash, which is also used to surround and enhance the form of the herons. The vessel is well potted of good clay with an unevenly applied glaze that runs and drips on the outside. The glaze is quite green and bubbly where thick. The potting on the whole is very thin for so large a dish.

19

DEEP DISH
Birds and peonies in underglaze blue
Arita ware, Imari type
2nd half 17th century
Diameter: 36.1 cm. Height: 6.2 cm. Foot: 17.0 cm.
Mr. and Mrs. Henry B. Pflager

This large Imari plate with its quiet design of resting birds and peony sprays probably comes from the developed phase of one of the Early Hizen kilns—perhaps Kuromuta. The flattened interior side, the broad-beaded brim and the use of the early geometric patterning on the brim are certainly related to the Nelson Gallery example (cat. no. 2), but the character of the glaze, body and especially the broad, well formed foot would indicate a date after 1650. The back of the dish is decorated sketchily with two designs of grapes, grape leaves and tendrils in underglaze blue. The center of the slightly domed base carries a central spur mark and a *fuku*-like mark within a double square. The character of the glaze, body and painting also relate this piece to the St. Louis plate with herons (cat. no. 18).

20
BOTTLE VASE
Underglaze blue and overglaze blue enamel
Arita ware, Imari type
18th century
Height: 23.9 cm. Diameter: 13.5 cm. Foot: 9.3 cm.
Mrs. Eugene W. Kettering

This very attractive small bottle is unusually decorated with a thick blue enamel covering the upper two-thirds of the vessel. The handsome, deep blue color of the enamel has been enriched by an underglaze blue wash applied beneath it. Counterbalancing the glassy blue is a broad band of reserved white with simple floral decoration. This chrysanthemum spray is painted in a light underglaze blue further softened by the thick, bubbly glaze. This bottle would normally be called Imari in style, but the qualities of the paste and the glaze suggest that it may have been potted at a Kakiemon kiln.

21
JAR
Decorated in underglaze blue
Arita ware, late 17th century
Height: 25.5 cm. Diameter: 20.3 cm. Foot: 12.2 cm.
City Art Museum of Saint Louis,
W. K. Bixby Oriental Art Trust Fund
1:68

This jar is decorated with a single sweeping chrysanthemum branch on which rests a *hoho* bird with a long, sweeping tail. The design is well conceived and beautifully drawn in a dark, rich cobalt blue. The drawing has been augmented by well modulated blue washes. Several jars of

the same design and similar size are known in private collections or in the hands of dealers. Jenyns illustrates one such belonging to Mr. Mayuyama in *Japanese Porcelain* (See ref. 14, pl. 12A) with a probable attribution to a Kakiemon kiln. Most of these jars vary both in the neck and shoulder ornamentation as well as in the quality of the rendering of the design. In this group there seems also to be a variety of ways of finishing the foot, which in none of the examples I have seen is particularly successful. The glaze is good, quite thick and rather bubbly. The paste is fine and speckled in appearance at both mouth and lip.

22
LARGE JAR
Floral designs in underglaze blue
Arita ware, Kakiemon type
Last half 17th century
Height: 47.0 cm. Diameter: 33.5 cm. Foot: 17.3 cm.
The Dayton Art Institute, Funds provided by
the Jefferson Patterson Endowment
69.46

This jar is a fine example of the blue and white Kakiemon style. The fine quality of the body and the superior decoration in the Kakiemon manner prompts the attribution. The major designs of tree, peony, rocks, orchid leaves and butterflies are well drawn in rich underglaze blue that tends to "heap-and-pile" somewhat in the outlines. The decoration on the shoulder of peony scrolling and precious objects is related to the contemporary blue and white wares derived from Wan Li prototypes (See cat. nos. 32 and 35). The repeating chrysanthemum petal form on the shoulder is unusual on a piece of blue and white presumed to have been produced prior to the Genroku era, but the ample evidence of the design on enameled pieces prior to Genroku in addition to the shape of the vessel and the rendering of the design elements would seem to make a Manji-Tenwa eras (1658-1683) dating reasonable.

23

LARGE, LOBED DISH
Decorated in underglaze blue
Arita ware, late 17th or 18th century
Diameter: 39.5 cm. Height: 8.3 cm. Foot: 22.2 cm.
Mr. and Mrs. John D. Rockefeller 3rd

It is difficult to assign a stylistic label to this plate as it has elements of both the Imari and Kakiemon types. The heavily potted body and the fairly wide footring appear in wares of the Imari type, yet the decoration is almost wholly Kakiemon. The design of pine, plum and bamboo with rocks and curving mounds is the same as that found on the many polychrome plates of the late 17th and early 18th century (See cat. nos. 87 and 88). Although the theme of flying geese is not particularly closely related to Kakiemon polychrome decoration, its composition certainly is. The design is well painted in rich, vivid blue washes with robustly drawn outlines. In many areas of the drawing, the thick underglaze blue has burned through the glaze giving fine character to the line. The back is decorated with the typical Kakiemon motif of small flower heads and running leafy scrolling drawn within parallel lines and washed with pale blue. The sides are slightly everted, and the lobed lip rim is softly rounded. Five fairly large spur marks are seen on the slightly convex base.

24

HEXAGONAL JAR
Garden designs in underglaze blue
Arita export ware, Ko-Imari type
Late 17th–early 18th century
Height: 41.3 cm. Diameter: 32.6 cm. Foot: 15.6 cm.
Mr. and Mrs. John A. Pope

Flower garden themes such as this were often used on early Imari large jars and are seen particularly on those with overglaze enamels. Usually some ground work, rocks, some sort of fence and other garden flowers are to be seen. Here the major design of peonies and chrysanthemums and their leaves are used to dominate the swelling form of the jar and the other elements are restricted to the lower third of the form. Panels of stylized floral forms and diaper pattern decorate the slightly tapering, high neck. This design is complimented just above the foot by a band of repeating peaked forms.

25

OCTAGONAL JAR
Boating scenes in underglaze blue
Arita export ware, Ko-Imari type
Late 17th–early 18th century
Height: 50.8 cm. Diameter: 40.7 cm. Foot: 20.0 cm.
Mr. and Mrs. John D. Rockefeller 3rd

This large and very handsome blue and white jar is an excellent example of the persistence of the scenic design modified by Japanese decorative taste. Unlike the fantastic scenes of the earlier wares, these boating groups are highly descriptive within the overall decorative scheme. The actions and attitudes of the figures in the boats are readily discernible, and the fantastic rocks and out-of-scale trees are used here to compliment the scene descriptively as well as decoratively. The intent of the representational design is known to the decorator and well integrated into the total design. Such designs are rare in Imari wares which usually were painted with more decorative designs of larger scale. Those with descriptive scenes are usually no more than vignettes within a decorative framework such as the large polychrome jars with *Ukiyo-e* derived designs. The straight neck of the jar is decorated with panels of auspicious symbols. The shoulder has a band of simple scrolling, a stylized chrysanthemum leaf band, and a section of dragons coursing through clouds separated from the main decoration by double lines. The base of the jar is simply decorated with triangular patterning and annular lines. The potting is well handled and quite thick. While of a typical Genroku shape, the body is rather more wide for the height than is usual. The underglaze blue is of good color and quite clean.

The jar is presumed to be of early Genroku date and perhaps made for a Japanese patron rather than for export.

26
BOTTLE
Vine leaf design in underglaze blue
Arita ware, Early Imari type
Late 17th–early 18th century
Height: 30.1 cm. Diameter: 7.1 cm. Foot: 10.0 cm.
Mr. and Mrs. Otto E. Nelson

This solidly formed bottle is simply decorated with a single design of a grape vine between blue lines on the body of the vessel. Around the bottom of the neck above double lines a *ju-i* motif is repeated. The freely drawn design is augmented by simple light and dark washes. The simplicity and vigor of the design is well suited to the handsome and sturdy form. The glaze is thick and quite clean. The bottom is glazed. Dating such bottles is not always easy as their pleasing form and simple functionalism caused them to be produced in many places over a long period of time. The form, design and color of the pigment would indicate that this example was probably made prior to the last decade or two of the century or, if as late as the Genroku era (1688-1703), in the manner of the earlier style.

PUBLISHED: Frank, Ann. *Chinese Blue and White.* New York: Walker and Company, 1969, p. 91.

27
BOTTLE
Pine tree design in underglaze blue
Arita ware, Imari type
Late 17th-early 18th century
Height: 36.5 cm. Diameter: 23.1 cm. Foot: 13.5 cm.
Eugene Fuller Memorial Collection,
Seattle Art Museum
68.J26.30

Among 17th and 18th century blue and white wares the truly unique piece is a rarity of which this superb bottle is a particularly fine example. The bottle is well potted in a full-bodied pear-shaped form. Although one would expect a bottle of this size and shape to be heavily potted, the very fineness of the potting is revealed by the light weight of the vessel. The decoration is extraordinary in both design and rendering. The motif of the old pine dominates the entire surface, rising from the annular line at the bottom of the vessel and spreading in deep curves around the body. The stylized boughs provide a pattern-on-pattern effect leading the eye along the branches as well as making interesting visual stops. At the base of the neck the bough and branch motif is repeated between lines providing a quality of weightiness to the primary design. It seems reasonable to suggest that the design was not painted by an ordinary porcelain painter because the technique is so unlike that found on other pots and so much more closely related to contemporary *sumi-e* styles. The painting is quite "wet" and in some respects is reminiscent of the finger painting technique used in both China and Japan. The concept of the gnarled old pine is enhanced by the use of a dark greyed blue pigment similar to that found on some of the Early Hizen *sometsuke* wares. The glaze is thick and somewhat drawn and pitted, particularly around the foot and at the lip.

28
DISH WITH EVERTED RIM
Fishnet design in underglaze blue
Arita ware, Imari type
2nd half 17th century
Diameter: 21.7 cm. Height: 4.6 cm. Foot: 13.0 cm.
Mrs. George H. Bunting, Jr.

Fishnet designs were among the earliest used on Early Hizen wares and have been used continually since then. The simple attractiveness of the design, its ease of execution and its relevance to the life of a fishing nation all combined to insure the persistence of the motif. Because of the long continuum of production, the dating of the wares is particularly difficult. The Early Hizen wares are usually recognizable by their body and the quality of the blue; but, after the early period, difficulties are compounded. Mrs. Bunting's most attractive example appears to be of 17th century date. The design is especially well drawn and covers the entire dish with the exception of the base, which is marked *Ta Ming Nien Chih.* These characters are rather crudely painted. The dish is well and thickly potted with an everted lip and a short, slightly rounded, flat foot.

29
LARGE PLATE
Leaf design in underglaze blue
Arita ware, Imari type
Early 18th century
Diameter: 36.6 cm. Height: 8.4 cm. Foot: 18.3 cm.
Nelson Gallery—Atkins Museum
63.4

The design of this early Imari piece is most unusual and satisfying. It is obvious that such a design was not made for export: its highly sophisticated abstract quality would not have suited the contemporary taste of Europe. The design is ingeniously composed of positive-negative leaf forms enriched with half-round scalloped forms on either side of the plate and a section of the same form wedged at the bottom. It has been suggested that these rounded forms with their spreading linear branches represent a stylized chestnut. The clean underglaze blue is painted with overlapping strokes on the leaf design and subtly shaded wash in the chestnut designs. The linear drawing is painted in a darker shade which runs to dark blue-black where it is particularly thick. The back is decorated with the precious object design. An unidentified *fuku*-like mark in a double square is placed asymetrically on the base. There are five fairly large spur marks, one central and four surrounding on the base. The foot is short, heavy, triangular in section and rounded on the unglazed bottom. A very similar piece is to be seen in *Old Imari* (See ref. 30, p. 350, pl. 88) and *Old Imari Blue and White Porcelain* (See ref. 35, pl. 285).

PUBLISHED: *Archives of the Chinese Art Society of America*, Vol. XVIII. New York: 1964, p. 79.

30
GOURD-SHAPED BOTTLE
Landscape designs in underglaze blue
Arita export ware
2nd half 17th century
Height: 28.4 cm. Diameter: 14.8 cm. Foot: 9.6 cm.
Mr. and Mrs. John A. Pope

The gourd shape with its five meandering molded panels and the designs of landscape and *takokarakusa* scrolling all reflect the direct influence of late Ming and Transitional wares. *Kraak-porselein* gourd bottles are known to have been shipped to Europe, and one occasionally sees them in early Dutch paintings. Demand in Europe for these vessels must have continued to be strong enough for the Japanese to be called upon to provide their own export version. The Dutch *Registers* mention the export of small gourd-shaped flasks in the year 1663 (See ref. 40, p. 148) so that again the Manji-Tenwa eras dating is applicable. The gourd-shaped bottle was not only an export form. The Japanese greatly admired the so-called *ko-sometsuke* and *shonzui* gourd bottles which they acquired from China and produced themselves in blue and white, a monochrome blue glaze and, eventually, in overglaze enamels. Most of the bottles produced for domestic use were apparently designed in the Transitional manner and were usually described as Ko-Kutani ware. They were generally smaller than those intended for export.

31
JAR
Landscapes with figures in underglaze blue
Arita export ware
2nd half 17th century
Height: 29.9 cm. Diameter: 24.6 cm. Foot: 12.5 cm.
Mr. and Mrs. John A. Pope

The decoration of this jar, like that of the other examples in this group, is in the Chinese manner. The design is separated into three groupings of figures divided by cliffs in clouds, banana trees, palm trees, brush pines and vegetation. The strange, other-worldly appearance of the figures is reinforced by the lush and exotic plants and the floating cloud forms supporting and separating the scenes. The sense of fantasy dominates the descriptive content of the decoration, adding a new dimension to the scene. As for the rest of this group, a Manji-Tenwa dating would seem appropriate.

32
BEER JUG WITH A SILVER LID
Reserves of landscapes in underglaze blue
Arita export ware
2nd half 17th century
Height: 27.0 cm. Width: 20.6 cm. Foot: 9.8 cm.
Mr. and Mrs. John A. Pope

Three large reserves separated by panels of floral scrolling contain landscapes painted after the late Ming or Transitional Chinese style. The central reserve opposite the handle contains two figures with an umbrella, houses and a running beast in a wooded landscape; to the left of it is a reserve of flying birds and birds resting on branches in a rocky landscape. The third reserve contains by far the most interesting landscape of the three and the one illustrated here. Vigorously painted with a naive misunderstanding of the Chinese model, this landscape of antediluvian birds, strange unstable mountains and bottle-brush trees becomes a scene of fantasy. The one reference to human habitation in the scene is the thatched hut in the center. It repeats the lines of the little peaked hills, reiterating the strange solitude and unreality of the landscape. Despite the mundane nature of the production of these early export wares, they often, as here, rise to a height of charm and vigor which probably was unintentional in their making and went unappreciated in their ultimate use. This vessel is virtually identical to the jug with a lid dated 1681 and published by Volker as a beer jug made from models sent to Japan from Holland in 1661. A reasonable dating would, therefore, be the Manji-Tenwa eras (1658-1683). The size of this piece would lead one to assume that it was used as a container for beer rather than as a drinking vessel. The

silver lid on the Pope jug has not been dated but appears to be of the early 18th century.

33
APOTHECARY BOTTLE
Floral and bird designs in underglaze blue
Arita export ware
Late 18th century
Height: 22.5 cm. Diameter: 17.3 cm. Foot: 11.3 cm.
Ralph M. Chait Galleries, Inc.

Bottles of this form are of European origin and were an important item of export by the Dutch East India Company. The forms were known in the trade as gallipots and were among the first European shapes to be exported. The first mention of their export is reported by Volker (See ref. 40, p. 125). In 1653, a large shipment of the gallipots was sent to the apothecary shop in Batavia. Jenyns points out that this was probably not the first export of the form (See ref. 14, p. 59). The form seems to have persisted throughout the rest of the century in either undecorated or blue and white wares. Volker, in his second book (See ref. 39, p. 28), records the mention of a white gallipot shipped in 1699 and gallipots are again mentioned in the *Registers* for 1711 (See p. 33 of the same source). A bottle of almost identical shape and design but of quite a bit larger size is in the Millikin Collection in Cleveland. That bottle was published by Martin Lerner in the *Bulletin of the Cleveland Museum of Art* (See ref. 20, p. 275) in which he makes excellent argument for the association of the initials J.C. on the bottom of the bottle with a certain Johannes Camphys who was in charge of Dutch affairs in Japan from 1671 to 1684. The attribution of Cleveland and, therefore, this bottle to Camphys' use would appear secure enough to date the pieces to the decade of his directorship in Japan (1760-1780). A bottle of similar design belonging to Sir Harry and Lady Garner is published by Jenyns (See ref. 14, pl. 10A) as Shoo-Empo period (1652-1680). An interesting pair of bottles in the Gerry Collection have the initials JVH on the body of each enclosed in a similar wreath (See ref. 37, pl. 14, cat. 45).

34

V.O.C. CHARGER
Underglaze blue decoration
Arita export ware
2nd half 17th century
Diameter: 39.0 cm. Height: 5.3 cm. Foot: 19.5 cm.
City Art Museum of Saint Louis,
W. K. Bixby Oriental Art Trust Fund
14:69

The central circular medallion with the initials "VOC" refers to the Dutch East India Company (Vereenigde Oostindische Companie) for whose use the plate was made. While important personages associated with the Company sometimes had personal services made with their initials worked into the design, the bulk of the wares used by the Company probably were indistinguishable from the other export wares. There is, however, a group of export porcelains that consists of good-sized plates bearing the initials of the Company. All of the known plates carry the same general design of two long-tailed birds with fruit and flowers in the center, and a separated panel of floral decoration on the brim. The design is a debased version of one found on late Ming Carrack ware. Although the design remains essentially the same, the quality of the rendering of the design varies considerably. Some examples, such as that in the Victoria and Albert Museum published by Jenyns (See ref. 14, pl. 14B), are quite carefully drawn; but, in general, most examples tend to look hurriedly painted with particular concern only for the ingredients of the design rather than an accomplished rendering of it. However, some of the more poorly painted specimens show a vitality of painting that is not uninteresting. Fine examples in American collections include a smaller plate in the Metropolitan Museum of Art, and one just a bit smaller than the St. Louis plate in the Center of Asian Art and Culture in San Francisco. Shards bearing the "VOC" and painted with the same designs have been excavated at the site of the Sarugawa kiln, and, therefore, most of the examples have been presumed to have come from that site (See

ref. 14, p. 61, and footnote reference to the shard illustrations in *Old Imari*). The Manji-Tenwa eras (1658-1683) dating for this and much of the comparable material would seem justified.

35

LARGE PLATE
Bee on rock design in underglaze blue
Arita export ware
2nd half 17th century
Diameter: 38.0 cm. Height: 7.0 cm. Foot: 18.2 cm.
Mrs. George H. Bunting, Jr.

The so-called *kraak-porselein* of the late Ming period was by far the greatest influence on the early Arita export wares. While the misunderstanding by the Japanese artist of the original Ming design motives changed the appearance and often the mood of the design, the essential elements were retained remarkably well. The central reserve of landscape, usually with an animal, bird or insect, framed in a geometric octagonal border, and usually with eight radiating panels of floral and precious object designs separated by smaller panels of jewels, bows, etc., is seen on almost all the wares. This plate is a particularly fine example of a Japanese rendering of the theme. While it remains an export piece, quickly painted according to a specific pattern, the quality of the rendering and use of the pigment make it more than satisfactory. The blue is rich and dark, providing good contrasts and interest within the design. The swift, sure hand of the painter has saved the piece from being dreary copy work. Too many of these export wares, particularly the smaller dishes, are almost completely without interest, being badly drawn in poor pigment with little attention to the fit of the decoration to the body. This fine plate is a happy relief from such wares. The plate is decorated on the back with a single line near the lip, and an allover open design of leafy scrollwork emanating from five simple flowers. The bottom shows chatter marks and there are five tiny spur marks, one central and four evenly placed in a square surrounding it.

36

LARGE PLATE
Overglaze polychrome enamel decoration
Arita export ware
2nd half 17th century
Diameter: 36.9 cm. Height: 7.6 cm. Foot: 17.2 cm.
Mr. and Mrs. John D. Rockefeller 3rd

The model upon which the decoration of this plate was fashioned is again the Chinese export wares of the late Ming period. The color scheme may have been taken from an original polychrome plate or applied to what was essentially a blue and white pattern. The latter would seem the more likely source. Japanese polychrome wares in the *kraak-porselein* style are rare by comparison with the more often seen blue and white wares. The brim of the plate is decorated in the familiar alternating floral and precious object motives separated by tassels and geometric bands. The central portion of the dish is decorated with a bouquet of three flowers and leaves rising from a vase with a diagonal fish scale pattern and an unreadable free-form device. The vase rests on a stand with pine, other floral forms and rockwork. This design theme is probably the precursor of the ubiquitous floral bouquet in a vase on a veranda pattern found on the later polychrome Imari style export wares.

37

HAND WARMER
Underglaze blue and overglaze enamels
Arita ware, Imari type
Late 17th century
Height: 14.2 cm. Width: 9.7 cm.
City Art Museum of Saint Louis,
W. K. Bixby Oriental Art Trust Fund
143:59

The quality of the porcelain, underglaze blue and red enamels of this piece are nearly identical with those of the deep plate (cat. no. 38). While the piece is of export style decoration and quality, it is probably not an export piece. The *shuro,* or handwarmer, was a particularly useful object in the badly heated Japanese home. It is decorated with simple designs in a muddy underglaze blue, thick red enamel and leafy scrollings in gold. The top is pierced in a flower form to facilitate the burning of the charcoal. A handle, now repaired, in the shape of the flower calyx is applied to the top and is the same brown found on the lip rims of dishes. The object rests on four triangular, short feet. While the quality of the decoration is not particularly fine, the shape is good and the porcelain itself is superior. It probably pre-dates the Genroku period by a few years.

38

DEEP PLATE
Underglaze blue, overglaze enamels and gold
Arita export ware, Ko-Imari type
Last quarter 17th century
Diameter: 31.0 cm. Height: 5.1 cm. Foot: 15.7 cm.
City Art Museum of Saint Louis,
W. K. Bixby Oriental Art Trust Fund
56:62

This plate is an example of the earliest of the *nishiki de* or brocade-patterned Imari wares which became so popular in Europe. The designs apparently came from the gorgeously decorated kimono of the period and the pattern books that came into use in the Kambun era (1661-1672). The design of this plate is more simple than is at first apparent, being a mirror image repeat of the same pattern on either half of the plate. The elements of *hoho,* or phoenix, paulownia leaves, plum, peony and chrysanthemum are met with constantly in this ware. The underglaze painting is in a dark, muddy, irregular blue. Several shades of overglaze red are used which vary from a rich, cherry red to a very light pinkish color. Parts of the design, particularly the birds' plummage are enriched by a thick, lacquer-like black enamel. Traces of gold are still present. The back of the plate is simply decorated by two floral stems in underglaze blue and iron red. The dish is heavily potted in the *kabuto-bachi* or helmet shape and has a very short, gritty foot. The base is glazed and has five fairly large spur marks, one central with the remaining four in the square about it. Unfortunately, the dish is in poor condition with much enamel and gold loss and a noticeable old crack in the center.

PUBLISHED: Old Imari Research Committee (ed.). *Old Imari.* Tokyo: Saga Kinkado, 1959, color pl. 15.

39
OCTAGONAL JAR
Underglaze blue and overglaze enamels
Arita ware, Imari type
Late 17th-early 18th century
Height: 41.0 cm. Diameter: 29.0 cm. Foot: 15.0 cm.
Mr. and Mrs. James B. Fisher, Jr.

Both sides of this large jar are pleasingly decorated with a design of weeping cherry tree rising out of a tripod bowl or stand. Augmenting this design and rising from the same source are a variety of different flowers, leaves and tendril forms filling the areas between the major designs. Eight lappet panels on the shoulder, conforming to the sides of the vessel, are filled with alternating designs of floral forms and palm trees seen above a railed platform. The flat-sided neck is decorated with peony flowers and stylized scrolling and clouds which are repeated above the footring. The decoration is primarily drawn in a dark, irregular underglaze blue with the addition of a rich iron red and some gold. The jar is well and heavily potted and has a short, slanting foot which is round on the bottom. The slightly convex base has one large spur mark at the bottom.

40
LARGE PLATE WITH SCALLOPED RIM
Underglaze blue with overglaze enamels
Arita export ware, Ko-Imari type
Late 17th-early 18th century
Diameter: 32.3 cm. Height: 5.2 cm. Foot: 7.1 cm.
The Metropolitan Museum of Art,
Gift of Charles Stewart Smith, 1893
93.3.110
Although of more sophisticated potting and design than the previous example, this plate has the same design peculiarity of mirror image repeat in the center of the plate. It will be noted that the scenic designs in the border and their interspacing floral decoration are identical in their designs. This tendency to mirror imaging and formally repeated designs, while probably expedient in these two examples, was to dominate the design of Imari wares until, in the period of great decline at the end of the 18th century, it was to become one of the major contributors to the triteness of the later wares. This plate is decorated with a rather dark, murky underglaze blue similar to the preceding example. In addition to the iron red and black enamel, a pale yellow and transparent green enamel are sparingly used. The back of the plate is decorated with a four-element peony flower and leafy scrolling pattern with a floral pattern border at the top of the foot. An enamel painted, floral sprig mark within a double circle is placed in the center of the bottom. Five fairly large spur marks, one central and four surrounding, are to be seen. A presumed Dresden collection incised mark N:155 over the symbol is in a wider blue circle on the bottom. The symbol beneath the number suggests that the plate had originally been marked as Green Chinese Porcelain with the symbol "I" and later corrected to mark the piece as Japanese which was symbolized by a "+." Even if we presume the Dresden mark to be of indubitable authenticity, the shakiness of the dating of the formation of the collection would make it a poor source for dating except insofar as the use of the cutoff date of 1741 is concerned. Jenyns discusses the problems of the Dresden marks in ref. 14, pp. 240-246. The de-

sign and physical qualities of the underglaze blue, enamels, and body suggest dating the plate to the Early Genroku era.

41
WINE BOTTLE
Floral and fan decoration in overglaze enamels
Arita ware, Imari type
2nd half 17th century
Height: 28.0 cm. Diameter: 9.6 cm. Foot: 6.7 cm.
Mathias Komor

Although this bottle has been formed with a long and extremely narrow neck the shape and potting of the body remain within the tradition of the strong and handsome forms of the blue and white and celadon bottles of the second quarter of the 17th century. While those earlier bottles lent themselves to simple decoration, the strength and assertiveness of their form did not take well to complex or extensive design schemes. The very elegant lightness of the form of this bottle, however, is eminently suited to decorative enrichment. The floral scrolling on the neck gives strength to the otherwise too spindly form, while the colorful bouquet of chrysanthemums and the well placed fan designs both repeat the graceful curves of the body and make its form more substantial. The designs are of course related to those associated with Kakiemon wares, but the colors, rendering and body would suggest another Arita kiln. The design indicates that it was painted *after* a Kakiemon one rather than the other way around. This in itself would indicate a dating in the 1670's or '80's when designs of the same order were used on Kakiemon export wares.

42
MODEL OF AN ACTOR
Overglaze enamel and gold decoration
Arita ware, Ko-Imari type
Late 17th century
Height: 31.2 cm. Width: (at base) 10.5 cm.
The Art Gallery of Greater Victoria,
Fred and Isabel Pollard Collection
63.50

Among the early export models of figures, those depicting men and animals seem to be the most rare. Figures of beauties in gorgeous kimonos were portrayed far more often. This interesting early figure is presumably that of an actor and was modeled directly rather than molded. The standing figure is dressed in a kimono decorated in the fashion made popular in the Kambun era and the over-kimono or *haori* carries designs of the *shou* character in gold and *kiri-mon* motives in overglaze enamels. The rendering and design of the decoration have elements of both Kakiemon and Ko-Imari styles. Figures were decorated in both styles in the period, but, whichever label one chooses to attach to the piece, it remains a fine example of the early Arita model style. While a dating of c. 1690 is usually applied to such examples, this particular one may slightly pre-date the Genroku era.

PUBLISHED: *Permanent Collection. The Art Gallery of Greater Victoria,* Fig. 15.

43
COVERED BOWL
Underglaze blue and overglaze enamels
Arita ware, *Kenjo* Imari type
1st half 18th century
Diameter: 22.0 cm. Height: 13.6 cm. Foot: 13.0 cm.
The Metropolitan Museum of Art,
Gift of Mrs. V. Everit Macy, 1923
23.225.134

This handsome presentation box is richly decorated in a color scheme that is primarily red, with green, aubergine, underglaze blue and touches of gold. Both cover and bowl are decorated with medallions against a stylized floral diaper pattern. The primary double medallions contain seated figures against a red background. The figures probably represent Japanese renderings of Taoist worthies. They are represented as a man reading from a scroll, a man seated with a broom and a crawling child with a top. The larger medallions are separated by scrolled cartouches with stylized floral forms. The top is decorated by a broad circle with medallions within and a flattened bow-shaped applied handle. The base has a spurious Wan Li mark in underglaze blue. The rich, matte quality of the overglaze red and the generally fine quality of the painting and design would indicate that this piece may have been produced around the middle of the 18th century.

PUBLISHED: James, F. S. *Macy Collection.* c. 1896, no. 166

FORMER COLLECTION: V. Everit Macy

44
PLATE
Underglaze blue and overglaze enamels and gold
Arita ware, *Kenjo* Imari type
Early 18th century
Diameter: 21.4 cm. Height: 3.6 cm. Foot: 14.9 cm.
The Mr. and Mrs. Severance A. Millikin
Collection, Courtesy of the Cleveland
Museum of Art

The central reserve of this plate is decorated with a scene of three Chinese figures on a veranda with trees, rocks, etc., and a short poem extolling the pleasures of spring. Underglaze blue with overglaze red, pink, black under green, and some ochre yellow and gold are used. The surrounding band of stylized scroll work and fish is painted solely in red with gold. Running beasts and precious object designs separated by cloud forms done in the Wan Li manner in underglaze blue and red decorate the exterior. The base has a large six-character Chia Ching mark and four spur marks, one central and three surrounding. The short, sloping, triangular foot shows a fine, hard white body on its thin, exposed base. The plate has a fine brown lip rim. The quality of the ware and the painting is of a consistently high order throughout.

45
BOTTLE
Underglaze blue and overglaze enamels
Arita ware, *Kenjo* Imari type
Early 18th century
Height: 24.8 cm. Diameter: 12.0 cm. Foot: 7.8 cm.
Mr. and Mrs. John A. Pope

This graceful bottle is comparable in quality to the previous example of *Kenjo* Imari and is decorated in the same color scheme of red, yellow and green, complimented by the underglaze blue. The decoration is a most sophisticated combination of natural forms, diaper patterns, motives taken from Ming porcelain and other conceived designs arranged together in a very elaborate but pleasing manner. The principal device in the underglaze blue cartouche is an early version of the helmet decoration device so often ill-used on late Imari wares.

46
DEEP BOWL WITH FLARING SIDES
Underglaze blue and overglaze enamels
Arita ware, Imari type
18th century
Diameter: 21.9 cm. Height: 7.9 cm. Foot: 8.8 cm.
The Metropolitan Museum of Art,
Gift of Charles Stewart Smith, 1893
93.3.408

The severity of the simple, flaring shape helps to contain the profusion of decoration of this bowl. By contrast with the interior, the outside is simply decorated with cartouches containing stylized floral forms separated by *hoho* birds with great, spreading tail feathers. What appears on the interior to be a number of different and complex designs is merely a very tightly designed repeat of two symetrical patterns with cloud scrolling between. The pattern is exactly repeated three times on the walls of the vessel with the only change being that of the colors. The enamels used are an ochre yellow, satin red, matte red, a very purple aubergine, greens, some gold and matte black in addition to the underglaze blue. The piece is marked on the base *"ki gyoku hotei no kin"* in underglaze blue within a large double circle. What appears to be a bowl of the same size and shape is published in *Old Imari* (See ref. 30, black and white pl. 79). Fedderson publishes a bowl from Vienna of the same shape and design scheme (See ref. 3, p. 85, fig. 59).

FORMER COLLECTION: Captain Frank Brinkley, cat. no. 301

47

TRIANGULAR BOWL
Figural decoration in underglaze blue
Arita ware, Imari type
Early 18th century
Diameter: 18.2 cm. Height: 10.9 cm. Foot: 9.8 cm.
Philadelphia Museum of Art,
Gift of Mr. and Mrs. Richard C. Bull
65-69-1

The surface of the bowl is separated into three panels, each decorated with figures as follows: a pair of standing figures in European dress against a diapered ground; a figure holding a gourd-shaped bottle; and a figure holding a flaming basket on a pole. This last figure scene may represent a figure holding the device used to light the water in nighttime cormorant fishing in Japan. The designs are carried out in outline form with dark and light washes against either the diaper patterning or the darker blue washed ground. The painting is vigorously done in a rich blue. The potting is fairly heavy and the paste is very white, fine and clean. The interior of the bowl and the base are undecorated.

48

LARGE BOWL
Underglaze blue and overglaze enamels and gold
Arita ware, Imari type
Late 18th–early 19th century
Diameter: 37.0 cm. Height: 12.0 Foot: 19.0 cm.
Philadelphia Museum of Art,
Gift of Mr. and Mrs. Ralph Balestrieri
63-47-2

These so-called "five ships" bowls were popular in the second half of the 18th century and continued to be produced through at least the first quarter of the 19th century. Their theme is a revival of the *Namban* or Southern Barbarian style which was so effectively used on screens in the early 17th century. The designs, as they are used here, consist of a foreign ship in a central reserve in the bottom of the interior surrounded on the sides by two rectangular reserves of ships, four pairs of standing European figures and a meaningless pair of heraldic arms. The whole is

set against a typical Imari diaper pattern. The outside is decorated similarly with two ships and two pairs of European figures in red medallions separated by peony flowers and leafy scrolling. The base is marked with a large *kotobuki (shou)* character in gold outlined in red. The color scheme of the bowl is iron red, black, aubergine, ochre yellow, green, gold and a mottled underglaze blue. A nearly identical example with the same type of high concave collar-like rim may be seen in *Old Imari* (See ref. 30, p. 210, fig. 36). The reference also illustrates the base with the *kotobuki* character (p. 134, fig. 50). The bowl is well and heavily potted, having a short, triangular foot and a flat base with five well placed spur marks. Most bowls of this design have a simple, flattened rim with a repeating design rather than the collar rim seen here.

49

BOTTLE VASE
Namban designs in overglaze enamels
Arita ware, Imari type
18th century
Height: 55.0 cm. Diameter: 33.6 cm. Foot: 15.0 cm.
The Cleveland Museum of Art,
Gift of Ralph King
19.837

This large and imposing gourd-shaped bottle is a *tour de force* of the Imari enamelers' art. Unlike most of the Imari wares no underglaze blue is used, instead, the drawing is mainly carried out in a matte black. The design motives used are all foreign in origin. Aside from the major designs of *Namban* ship and standing figures, the beloved Dutch tulip recurs in the design at the mouth of the vessel, in more stylized form in the upper reserves, in the pink borders, on the neck, and in a striking manner in black on the base. The only element in the decoration which is remotely Japanese is the highly stylized *hoho* bird whose tail feathers enclose the ship design —and even this element bears little resemblance to the traditional manner of rendering the form. It has been suggested that the tulip design on the base was added either in the Dutch East Indies or in Holland (See ref. 19, p. 12). This would seem doubtful as the color and texture of the black enamel and the manner and design of the drawing are so similar to that on the bottle.

PUBLISHED: Lee, Sherman E. *The Japanese Decorative Style.* Cleveland: The Cleveland Museum of Art, 1961, p. 124, fig. 148.

Lee, Sherman E. *A History of Far Eastern Art.* New York: Harry N. Abrams, Inc., 1964, p. 496, fig. 654.

Mikami, Tsugio. *Toki.* Tokyo: 1968, pl. 12 and fig. 137.

Federson, Martin. *Japanese Decorative Art.* Translated by Katherine Watson. New York: Thomas Yoseloff, 1962, p. 84, fig. 58.

50
LARGE DISH

Landscape design in underglaze blue
Kutani type, late 17th century
Diameter: 44.0 cm. Height: 8.0 cm. Foot: 18.0 cm.
Mrs. George H. Bunting, Jr.

This inventive and distinguished landscape design has been attributed to the hand of Morikage, a *Kano* school painter who was a pupil of Tan-yu and who is supposed to have been active at the end of the 17th century. He is thought to have resided at Kanazawa at one time and to have had an influence on the designs of Kutani wares. Jenyns, among others, has doubted this (See various references under "Potters" in *Japanese Porcelain,* ref. 14). Whether Morikage's influence on Kutani wares is truth or myth, the landscape on this plate has been associated with his name by Japanese scholars whose familiarity with his style cannot be dismissed. Proof of a Morikage association with this dish would be of interest, as would evidence of a Kaga Ko-Kutani association. However, neither would affect the quality manifest in the object itself. The dish is thinly potted but not finely finished, and it has warped badly in the firing. The back is simply decorated by two landscapes painted with economy and swiftness yet complete within themselves and beautifully fitted to the form. A *fuku* mark within a double square is seen in the center of the

base. The glaze appears a warm, creamy white, somewhat matte in texture. The wide footring is rounded on the bottom and there are indications of tiny spur marks on the base.

51
GOURD-SHAPED BOTTLE

Pine and plum in overglaze enamels
Arita ware, Ko-Kutani type
Height: 24.8 cm. Diameter: 17.1 cm. Foot: 9.5 cm.
Mr. and Mrs. John D. Rockefeller 3rd

This bottle has been given an Arita provenance primarily on the basis of the glaze and potting of the foot which bear great similarity to other Arita wares such as the large Metropolitan Museum bottle (cat. no. 52). The overglaze enamels are, however, different from that color scheme and are more closely allied to those of the large Shonzui style plate from Seattle (cat. no. 54). The bottle gourd shape was a favorite one for Japanese *tokuri* and this is a particularly fine example of the shape. It is heavy bodied with the waist encircled with molded rope decoration and the thin, slightly flaring neck decorated with a molded bee. The overglaze decoration of pine and plum tree in green, blue, ochre yellow and aubergine is surrounded by abstract cloud forms with lattice-like patterning in a matte, dark cherry red. The rather heavy decoration is well suited to the swelling pear shape of the body on its relatively narrow foot rim. The foot rim is straight and poorly finished on the bottom. The glaze is thick and milky white with no natural crackle.

52
LARGE BOTTLE

Decorated with overglaze enamels
Arita ware, Ko-Kutani type
2nd half 17th century
Height: 38.9 cm. Diameter: 19.9 cm. Foot: 12.7 cm.
The Metropolitan Museum of Art,
Gift of Charles Stewart Smith, 1893
93.3.109

Of the many different classes of wares attributed to the Kutani kilns the group of porcelains represented by this bottle are among the most striking in decoration. The group is characterized by the predominate use of a rich dark red, a clean ochre yellow, turquoise and sometimes aubergine enamels over a thick, milky white glaze. Many of the group have a hatching in red as a background for the other design elements, as this bottle does, which is decorated with a theme of clouds and cherry blossoms. Jenyns publishes a group of this type (See ref. 14, pls. 82 and 83), among which is the now famous de la Mare ewer with a Dutch silver lid dated 1671. Jenyns dates the whole group to the Shoo-Kambun eras. The bottle came to The Metropolitan Museum with a mid-18th century dating which seems far too late for the physical and design qualities of the piece. The 2nd half of the 17th century dating should be sufficiently broad to encompass its production. The vessel is quite heavily potted and has a high, straight foot which is crudely finished on the bottom. The base is glazed but unmarked.

FORMER COLLECTION: Captain Frank Brinkley, cat. no. 254.

53
DISH
Underglaze blue and overglaze enamels
Ko-Kutani type, 17th century
Diameter: 30.7 cm. Height: 6.3 cm. Foot: 17.2 cm.
The Cleveland Museum of Art,
Gift from various Donors by Exchange
60.174

The simply stated design of pheasant on a rock with bamboo and floral forms against the large, circular open space is well framed by the active border of intertwining leafy scrolling. This type of design scheme in which compositions of quiet stability are juxtaposed with designs of great vitality and motion is characteristic of many of the wares of the Kutani type and accounts in no small part for the highly successful quality of their decoration. This dish is potted well but not finely finished. The sides recurve from the foot to the everted rim which is finished with a thin vertical beading and a flattened lip rim. It is enameled in a pale blue, aubergine, ochre

yellow and turquoise over a milky white, somewhat matte glaze. The back of the dish is decorated with three designs of a single flower in yellow with scrolling in aubergine. A small Ch'eng Hua (?) mark within a double square under an aubergine glaze is centered on the base. The only underglaze blue used is in the circle on the base and in the two bow lines on the foot. The foot is short and curves inward with a cut bottom. The glaze inside and out is somewhat matte with considerable accretion of foreign matter on the inside from the firing. The base shows three tiny spur marks triangulated about the center.

PUBLISHED: Lee, Sherman E. *The Japanese Decorative Style.* Cleveland: The Cleveland Museum of Art, 1961, p. 128, fig. 158.

54
DEEP DISH
Underglaze blue and overglaze enamels
Ko-Kutani type
Late 17th century
Diameter: 32.1 cm. Height: 6.7 cm. Foot: 18.8 cm.
Eugene Fuller Memorial Collection,
Seattle Art Museum
52.J27.8

This example represents a type of Ko-Kutani which is exceedingly rare outside of Japan, and is of its type among the finest in quality to be found anywhere. This type of ware belongs to a category of Kutani styled wares usually called colored *Shonzui* ware. The circular medallions or *marumon* and the landscape center were among the motives seen in the Chinese Transitional wares attributed to the legendary Shonzui and so much appreciated by the tea masters in Japan. This dish is decorated on the interior with a Chinese landscape in overglaze enamels of a brilliant blue, turquoise, muddy ochre, dull matte red, black and aubergine colors. The *marumon*, the triangular motives between them, and the large circle of double lines are painted in underglaze blue with the addition of the enamel colors within the circular designs. The back of the dish is decorated with four sprays of plum painted mostly in underglaze blue with a degraded red that is almost a maroon hue and a green that is the color of K'ang Hsi apple green. The body is well potted with a rounded, wavy lip rim and short, cut foot. The glaze is creamy white and uncrackled. The exterior in particular shows the glaze to be uneven and flocculent. The interior of the dish is humped up in the center. The base is marked with the character seen on the back of the Millikin Ao-Kutani dish (See cat. no. 64) but with a transposition of two of the characters within the double square.

55
DEEP PLATE
Peony design in overglaze enamels
Ao-Kutani type, 17th–18th century
Diameter: 37.7 cm. Height: 8.1 cm. Foot: 15.8 cm.
The Cleveland Museum of Art,
Purchase from the J. H. Wade Fund
60.224

The peony flowers and buds here are painted in aubergine, the leaves in green, and the background in yellow. The enamels used are thinner than on many Ao-Kutani examples giving this piece a softer, more subdued appearance. Extensive linear drawing in a dark brown pigment in the floral design and background imbrication also is a factor in softening the hue and tone of the enamels. The clean, simple shape of the plate and the serene quality of the design with its subtle coloration make this a most satisfying example of the Kutani style. An interesting, open scrolling in green and aubergine decorates the back. The base is simply decorated with dark brown allover scrolling under a green glaze. The exposed underglaze is a warm, greyed, creamy white with a regular crackle. The piece is fairly thickly potted and has a short, rounded foot burned slightly pink at the bottom.

PUBLISHED: Lee, Sherman E. *The Japanese Decorative Style.* Cleveland: The Cleveland Museum of Art, 1961, p. 129, fig. 161.

Mayuyama, Junkichi. *Japanese Art in the West.* Tokyo: Mayuyama and Company, 1966.

56
LARGE DISH
Decorated with overglaze enamels
Ao-Kutani style, late 17th century
Diameter: 36.5 cm. Height: 9.0 cm. Foot: 16.5 cm.
The Detroit Institute of Arts,
L. A. Young Fund
64.154

Although this dish has a superficial resemblance to the Ko-Kutani style Cleveland and Seattle dishes (cat. nos. 53 and 54) in the colors of enamels used and the formation of the vessel itself, it is more closely akin to the Ao-Kutani wares—particularly to the Cleveland dish (cat. no. 55). There are marked similarities in the size, shape and back decoration of the two. The thick and lustrous enamels are painted on a creamy white, crackled glaze that is fairly thick on the inside but quite thin on the back. The unevenly applied glaze on the back reveals considerable dripping and shows the marks where the glazer's hands held the vessel. A *fuku* mark is to be seen in the center of the base under a green glaze. The short, rounded foot apparently suffered in the firing and has burnt a brown color of a texture with none of the appearance of porcelain. Through an unfortunate accident there is a chip loss in the rim that shows the body as it truly exists—a fine grained, white porcelain or porcelaneous ware.

PUBLISHED: "Japanese Art in the Detroit Institute of Arts," *Bulletin of the Detroit Institute of Arts.* 1965, Vol. 44, no. 3, p. 58.

57
LARGE DISH
Melon design in overglaze enamels
Ao-Kutani type, 17th–18th century
Diameter: 38.0 cm. Height: 8.0 cm. Foot: 18.0 cm.
City Art Museum of Saint Louis,
Gift of Mr. and Mrs. Arthur B. Baer
14:66

The most unusual aspect of this dish is the treatment of the vine and tendril designs in the center. The dark brown pigment has been scratched and rubbed away to reveal the underglaze and then washed over with a pale aubergine glaze. While leaving the white underglaze exposed in a reserve design is not uncommon (cat. nos. 58 and 60), enameling over it appears rarely. The central decoration of melons, leaves, vines and tendrils shows great spirit and movement in its design, complimented by the counter-clockwise swirling of the leaf forms on the brim and cavetto. The melons and leaves are painted with a thick, brilliant green enamel against the background of dark aubergine and its lighter designs. The leaves at the edges are also green and the circle-patterned background is a pale yellow. The dark brown underdrawing appears black under the green enamel and pale brown under the yellow. The rim is finished with a rounded beading edged in brown. There is also a circular beading in the body at the base of the cavetto. The short, rounded foot has been ridged on the wheel much in the manner of K'ang Hsi wares and is pink at the bottom. The back has the ubiquitus design of rosettes under a thin, matte blue-green glaze. A large *fuku* mark of the same character as the Munsterberg plate (cat no. 61) is located in the center of the glazed but undecorated base.

PUBLISHED: *City Art Museum of Saint Louis Bulletin*, Vol. II, no. 2. St. Louis: 1966, cover and p. 1.

58
DEEP DISH
Gourd and leaf design in overglaze enamels
Ao-Kutani type, 17th–18th century
Diameter: 39.0 cm. Height: 9.2 cm. Foot: 16.5 cm.
Mr. and Mrs. John D. Rockefeller 3rd

This dish, like the bowl illustrated in color (cat. no. 60), uses the white underglaze in reserve for dramatic contrast in the design. The central bottle gourd dominates the composition in its stark simplicity. Around it, the curving tendrils, almost floating leaves and the emerging bottle gourd create a design of great movement against the patterned background. The leaves are painted with a thick, rich blue enamel and the background is mustard yellow. The underdrawing is

painted in a brown-black enamel which appears brown under the yellow glaze and black under the blue. The back is painted with an allover rosette pattern under a blue-green glaze. The base has no patterning but does have a small *fuku* mark within a double square and three spur marks. The foot is thick, slanted and flat on the bottom.

59
LARGE PLATE
Ko-Kutani type, late 17th century
Diameter: 40.6 cm. Height: 8.3 cm. Foot: 14.0 cm.
Center of Asian Art and Culture,
The Avery Brundage Collection,
M. H. de Young Memorial Museum
B66 P36

Kutani wares are often characterized by the robust quality of their decoration. This is certainly the case of this handsome piece. The often seen "three friends" motif here is forged into a landscape scene. The pine, plum and bamboo spring forth from little islands of rockwork. The oversize needles, blooms and leaves are painted in green and ochre yellow. The tree trunks and rockwork are enameled with aubergine and a brilliant, but pale, blue. The back is painted with two large designs of flowers and scrolling in aubergine and yellow and there is a *fuku*-like mark within a double square on the base covered by yellow glaze. The dark brown underpainting is vigorously drawn throughout. The glaze shows an allover crackle which is similar to both the Detroit and Cleveland dishes (See cat. nos. 56 and 55). In spite of the great differences in design between the three dishes, they share some physical similarities which cannot be ignored. The glaze, size, shape, manner of exterior decoration, and some similarities in the potting of the feet are perhaps worth further investigation.

PUBLISHED: Schöbel, Heinz. *The Four Dimensions of Avery Brundage.* Leipzig: 1968.

Ceramic Society of Japan. *Tosetsu.* January, 1966, color pl. 1.

60

LARGE BOWL
Banded leaf design in overglaze enamels
Ao-Kutani type, 17th–18th century
Diameter: 33.7 cm. Height: 8.1 cm. Foot. 16.3 cm.
Private Collection

The vigorous motion of the design of this sheaf of banded leaves is ingeniously emphasized by leaving the curving stem shapes free of overglaze enamel, thus providing great visual contrast between the white underglaze and the dark background of the design. This design is set against a patterning which could be either stylized fan or pine needle motif. The exterior is painted with an allover rosette pattern in black under a pale, blue-green, sticky glaze. The bowl is sturdily potted, and the short, rounded foot has been burned pink in the firing. The inside bottom and the base are both slightly convex. The bowl is unmarked.

PUBLISHED: Tokyo National Museum, *Exhibition of Important Kutani Wares.* Tokyo: 1967, no. 37, illustrated.

61

PLATE
Fan designs in overglaze enamels
Ao-Kutani type, 17th–18th century
Diameter: 21.4 cm. Height: 3.6 cm. Foot: 13.0 cm.
Dr. Hugo Munsterberg

This most attractive plate is probably from a set of such plates as nearly identical examples with similar wear marks may be seen in both the Millikin and Gerry Collections (See refs. 37, no. 166, and 37, no. 68, pl. 19). The design of the partial views of two opened fans and one closed fan is set against a field of bamboo or grass-like hatching. The entire color scheme is green and black except for the ochre yellow and brown design on the opened fan and the strip of yellow on the unopened one. The back of the plate is decorated with three chrysanthemums, and sketchily drawn leafy scrolling covers the rest of the surface. This design is painted in brown under a mustard glaze as is the mark within the double square in the center of the base. The plate has a brown, slightly rounded lip rim. The footring is very short on the outside and about twice as deep on the inside. It is straight, slightly rounded and burned pink on the bottom.

PUBLISHED: Munsterberg, Hugo. *Art of the Far East.* New York: Harry N. Abrams, Inc., 1968, p. 248 (in color)

62

SQUARE PLATE
Camellia design in overglaze enamels
Ao-Kutani type, 17th–18th century
Width: 17.6 cm. Height: 3.0 cm. Foot: 10.9 cm.
Eugene Fuller Memorial Collection,
Seattle Art Museum
56. J27.43

This small plate is one of the better known Japanese porcelains in American collections. The serene beauty of its design, the freshness of the drawing and the brilliance of the overglaze enamels have justly earned it great esteem. The camellia blooms are glazed with a rich, transparent amethyst hue; the leaves and the borders are a clean blue-green and the background is a warm ochre yellow. The back is painted with tightly repeated rosettes under the blue-green glaze. The lip rim is flat and brown. The short, thin, slanted foot is undecorated and flat on the bottom. The base is undecorated and shows one central spur mark. The foot shows a hard, grey paste.

PUBLISHED: *Japanese Art in the Seattle Art Museum.* Seattle Art Museum, 1960, no. 163.

Lee, Sherman E. *The Japanese Decorative Style.* Cleveland: The Cleveland Museum of Art, 1961, p. 129 and illus., p. 162, p. 153.

Japanese Art of the Edo Period. Nelson Gallery of Art, Kansas City, and City Art Museum, St. Louis: 1958, p. 19, no. 58.

63

LOBED, FOOTED DISH
Peony sprays in overglaze enamels
Ao-Kutani type, 17th–18th century
Diameter: 25.5 cm. Height: 6.5 cm. Foot: 15.0 cm.
Philadelphia Museum of Art,
The General Hector Tyndale
Memorial Collection
97-199

Like the other examples of Ao-Kutani style in the exhibition, this dish is decorated in a dark brown pigment under aubergine, green and yellow glazes. The central mirror of peony spray against a wood grain-like design in brown and yellow is nicely framed by the deeply notched and molded brim which is done in a black and green moire pattern. The wood grain patterning is particularly effective in the background of the central design where it provides an active foil for the simple curves and lush forms of the peony motif. The underbrim is decorated in black scrollwork under a transparent glaze and the outside of the foot rim is painted with a leaf design. The base is marked with *fuku* within a double square. The foot is high, straight and flat on the bottom. The flat lip rim is brown.

64

DEEP DISH
Leafy branch design in overglaze enamels
Ao-Kutani type, 17th–18th century
Diameter: 33.3 cm. Height: 6.1 cm. Foot: 16.7 cm.
The Mr. and Mrs. Severance A. Millikin Collection,
Courtesy of The Cleveland Museum of Art

This extraordinary plate is decorated with a unique design of a central branch in a brilliant blue with large, dark, almost emerald green leaves. This design is placed against a background of delicate, feathery scrollwork in brown under an ochre yellow glaze. All of the enamels are brilliantly clear and glassy. The back of the plate is decorated with a peony and leafy scroll pattern interrupted and generally obscured by the thick turquoise blue overglaze. The sides of the footring are also overglazed and the *fuku* mark on the base is much obscured in the same manner as the back design. The lip rim is a flat, matte

brown. The thin, straight foot slopes inward and is flat on the bottom.

PUBLISHED: Lee, Sherman E. *The Japanese Decorative Style.* Cleveland: The Cleveland Museum of Art, 1961, no. 160.

Jenyns, Soame. *Japanese Porcelain.* New York: Frederick A. Praeger, 1965, pl. 102.

65

LARGE, DEEP DISH
Peony and bird design in overglaze enamels
Ao-Kutani type, 17th–18th century
Diameter: 45.0 cm. Height: 10.5 cm. Foot: 19.0 cm.
Nelson Gallery—Atkins Museum
64.28

This exceptionally large and handsome example of the Ao-Kutani style has a decoration of peony leaves and blooms with a perched bird in aubergine and green enamels set against a patterned background of circular floral forms that appear brown under a yellow glaze. The decoration on the back is of chrysanthemum flowers with leafy scrolling in black under a somewhat glassy turquoise glaze. These designs, along with the *fuku* mark on the bottom, are painted in black under the glaze. The overglaze enamels on the interior are thick and glassy with some crackle. The aubergine enamel is a brilliant amethyst color. The underglaze is quite white and, in the interior, shows no apparent crackle. The dish is supported by a short, slanted foot with a flat base, and the lip rim is flat and brown.

PUBLISHED: *Archives of the Chinese Art Society of America,* Vol. 19. New York: 1965, p. 83, fig. 28.

66

SMALL PLATE
Chestnut design in overglaze enamels
Ko-Kutani type, late 17th or 18th century
Diameter: 14.6 cm. Height: 2.3 cm. Foot: 8.2 cm.
Center of Asian Art and Culture,
The Avery Brundage Collection,
M. H. de Young Memorial Museum
B64 P25

This very finely potted small dish is decorated with a central spray of chestnuts in a burr painted in green, blue, aubergine and a warm ochre yellow and outlined in black. The smooth, concave brim has three designs of pine needles in red with green. The enamels are thick, clear and iridescent. The foot is short and very thin. A square *fuku* mark is drawn in the center of the base and covered with green enamel. The base also has one central spur mark. It is presumed that this dish and the medallion dish from Honolulu are closely related.

67
SMALL PLATE
Decorated in overglaze enamels
Ko-Kutani type, late 17th or 18th century
Diameter: 14.6 cm. Height: 1.9 cm. Foot: 9.3 cm.
Honolulu Academy of Arts
3555.1

This handsome little plate is closely related to the Brundage plate (cat. no. 66) in its potting, smooth white glaze and in the color and quality of the overglaze enamels. The plate is decorated with two *marumon* in and projecting from the almost semicircular field of floral and tendril pattern. In the remaining reserved area two well drawn and judiciously positioned butterflies lightly echo the more heavily designed *marumon* in the lower field. The colors used are the same as those of the Brundage plate. On the back a small, square *fuku* mark is covered by a green glaze. Three designs of floral sprays are painted in enamel on the confined area between the top of the foot rim and the lip. The plate is finely potted and thinly glazed. The bottom is quite flat, and the lip rim is turned sharply but smoothly upward. While this class of wares may belong to the 17th century, I feel that an early 18th century date would be a more realistic assumption.

68
DISH WITH EVERTED RIM
Fish design in underglaze blue
Ko-Kutani type, late 17th or 18th century
Diameter: 21.0 cm. Height: 2.5 cm. Foot: 11.8 cm.
Philadelphia Museum of Art,
Given by R. G. Rincliffe
69-212-1

The decoration of this dish is perhaps too explicit for Western taste, but for a people to whom fish in public and private ponds are a daily sight, its design is both accurate and pleasing. However we react to the design, we can certainly appreciate the painting which is rendered in a natural and spontaneous manner with a fine, clean blue under the glaze. The dish is thinly potted with an everted lip, shallow, smooth cavetto and flat bottom. The foot is short, thin and curved inward. On the bottom is a crudely drawn *fuku* mark in underglaze blue and one central spur mark. The back is decorated with sprigs of plum blossom. The glaze is thin and milky white in appearance.

69
TWO DISHES
Singing bird designs in underglaze blue
Arita ware, Ko-Kutani type
2nd half 17th century
Diameter: 14.5 cm. Height: 2.7 cm. Foot: 9.3 cm.
Dr. Harold P. Stern

These small dishes are related to the dishes with molded border designs Jenyns has published as being perhaps the products of the Iwakawachi kiln's first phase (See ref. 14, pls. 9A and B). These plates are somewhat smaller than those referred to in Jenyns, but the manner of the decoration, especially the border molded with stylized characters, would seem to tie them to the same group whatever the place of manufacture. The dishes are quite thinly potted with a slightly scalloped rim and a high, thin foot. The base is decorated with one undeciphered *kanji* which is poorly drawn. One single spur mark is seen in the center of the base. The design is a simple one of great charm and is painted with sensitivity and vigor. The double circle enclosing the design is unusual. It is washed with blue and is most effective in setting off the design. It is the charm and vigor of the decoration which apparently has caused these and so many other small pieces of quality to earn the appellation of Ko-Kutani. The term, if inaccurate, is at least indicative of a taste, a quality and a style.

70

DISH WITH MOLDED BORDER
Bamboo design in underglaze blue
Arita ware, Ko-Kutani type
Diameter: 21.2 cm. Height: 2.4 cm. Foot: 14.0 cm.
Private Collection

Like the two small dishes belonging to Dr. Stern, this dish is related in terms of the molded border and treatment of the underglaze blue decoration to the group supposedly associated with the early phase of the Iwakawachi kiln. The dish is well painted with a design of bamboo in a rich, fairly dark blue. The border of swirling elements in low relief is covered by a very pale and somewhat matte celadon glaze. The back is undecorated except for a crudely drawn *fuku* mark in the center of the base. The dish is well potted with a slightly everted lip and a short, fairly thin triangular foot. The body paste and glaze of this piece would indicate that there is some relationship with the Philadelphia dish with design of fish (cat. no. 68).

71

BOTTLE
Floral decoration in underglaze blue
Arita ware, 2nd half 17th century
Height: 33.0 cm. Diameter: 19.0 cm. Foot: 12.7 cm.
The Baltimore Museum of Art
Gift of Mrs. Mason Knox from the
Estate of Miss Julia Rogers
45.22.4

The shape, glaze and decoration of this bottle are of considerable interest, for in combination they do not conform to the general run of Arita

blue and white wares of the 17th and 18th centuries. At first glance, the vessel might appear to be from a Kakiemon kiln, but the soft crazed glaze, the color of the blue, and the method of painting the floral and rock forms make this unlikely. The only apparently similar example in blue and white is the de la Mare bottle that Jenyns published originally as Ko-Kutani and more recently publishes in *Japanese Porcelain* as "Arita ware (Ko-Kutani style)" (See ref. 14, p. 198). Many of the polychrome wares attributed to the Kutani kiln are characterized by the same short-necked, bulbous shape and a similar crazing of the glaze. This, of course, does not suggest a Ko-Kutani attribution for this vessel but certainly calls for a closer examination of the bodies, glazes and decoration of both blue and white and polychrome wares displaying the same characteristics, in the hopes that enough corroborating data may present itself to identify the kiln site positively when and if the shards appear. Also of interest is the design on the neck of the bottle which consists of *kiri mon*—not of the Imperial type—and four-pointed devices with a square at their center. The meaning of this latter device, if indeed it has any, has not been determined. The neck of the bottle is finished with a double line, a band of neatly spaced cherry blossoms, a single line and a well drawn border of contiguous *ju-i* motives. This motif again is associated with the Arita-Kutani group of bottles and jars, but is hardly unique to it.

72

JAR
Underglaze blue decoration
Arita ware, Ko-Kutani type
2nd half 17th century
Height: 33.5 cm. Diameter: 27.4 cm. Foot: 13.4 cm.
Los Angeles County Museum of Art,
Ernest Larsen Blanck Memorial Collection
63.15

The large, full-bodied jar is painted with four vertical panels with scenes of a bird on a branch, a hermit and sprays of chrysanthemum and peony. Grapes with leaves and vines are seen between the panels. A band of plum blossoms encircles the shoulder with the remaining decoration being geometric floral patterning. The handling of the design and rendering are skillful throughout and particular finesse is seen in the drawing with the rich, dark cobalt blue. The glaze is thick and somewhat flocculent on the lower half of the vessel. The potting, the paste and particularly the foot would point to an Arita origin painted with a superb and original, if not unique, design in the Kutani manner.

73
JAR
Floral designs in overglaze enamels
Arita ware, Ko-Kutani type
2nd half 17th century
Height: 30.1 cm. Diameter: 24.9 cm. Foot: 12.4 cm.
City Art Museum of Saint Louis,
Gift of Mr. and Mrs. Arthur B. Baer
75:68

Wares of this type were formerly considered to be products of the Kutani kilns. However, this group is now generally accepted as the work of one of the Arita kilns in the second half of the 17th century, probably in the Shoo-Kambun eras (1652-1672). In both body and glaze the group is related to the early Kakiemon style jars such as that belonging to Dr. Stern. Although in this country few collections contain examples of this group, those found are of superior quality, among them the Chicago jar in the exhibition (cat. no. 74) and the very large and handsome bottle in the Freer Gallery illustrated by Jenyns (See ref. 14, pl. 84B). The wares are characterized by the use of pale overglaze enamels in blue-green, yellow and aubergine with some black drawing and an extensive use of rich, matte cherry red. This jar is divided into four reserves by lattice-like panels whose design is also seen in a modified version on the shoulder of the Chicago jar. The shoulder of this jar is painted with four floral designs in cartouches separated by a repeating wave pattern. The floral designs are quite naturally composed and competently

rendered. The glaze is thinly applied to the somewhat speckled body giving the appearance of a warm, creamy white surface.

PUBLISHED: *City Art Museum of Saint Louis Bulletin,* Vol. IV, no. 6 (March-April, 1969), cover and p. 1.

74
JAR
Peony design in overglaze enamels
Arita ware, Ko-Kutani type
2nd half 17th century
Height: 29.2 cm. Diameter: 23.6 cm. Foot: 13.1 cm.
Robert Allerton Collection,
The Art Institute of Chicago
59.6

In all the physical aspects of paste, potting, glaze and enamels this jar is identical with the St. Louis jar (cat. no. 73). The same design scheme of cartouches with floral designs divided by an imbricated pattern is seen on the shoulder. The design of the main decoration is, however, quite different in its intention. Instead of wildly growing floral forms within a formal framework, the decoration here flows smoothly around the jar emphasizing its shape. The well painted peony leaves and blooms make an interesting and moving pattern about the surface.

PUBLISHED: Lee, Sherman E. *The Japanese Decorative Style.* Cleveland: The Cleveland Museum of Art, 1961, p. 120, pl. 138.

EXHIBITED: Exhibition of Kakiemon ware held by the Japan Ceramic Society, Tokyo, May, 1959.

75
SMALL PLATE
Wave design in overglaze blue
Suisaka ware, late 17th or 18th century
Diameter: 13.1 cm. Height: 1.5 cm. Foot: 8.1 cm.
Private Collection

Unlike the Brundage Suisaka plate this small piece has a dark matte glaze covering all but the footring. This glaze is similar to that on a stoneware Suisaka plate in the Cleveland Museum (See ref. 19, p. 127, pl. 155). The only decoration is that of highly stylized ocean waves in a thick, transparent overglaze blue. The piece is very finely potted but shows almost intentional chatter marks from the finishing on the under-side. The foot is fairly high, thin and similar to that on the Brundage example. There is a single central spur mark on the base.

76
SMALL PLATE
Heron design in underglaze blue
Suisaka ware, late 17th or 18th century
Diameter: 15.0 cm. Height: 2.2 cm. Foot: 9.2 cm.
Center of Asian Art and Culture,
The Avery Brundage Collection,
M. H. de Young Memorial Museum
B62 P18

These small dishes are relatively rare in American collections. They are purported to be the wares of the Suisaka kiln near Kutani in old Kaga. Whether this is true or not can only be conjectured, in any event they do not seem to be typical of any Arita wares in body or design. This handsome plate has a charming design of a heron on one leg and clouds painted in underglaze blue on a white reserved ground. The remaining decoration of willow and grass is painted in iron oxide in much the same manner as it is used in Shino wares. With the exception of the re-served areas the piece is completely covered with a glassy, yellowish brown glaze. The potting is good and finely done. The base shows one central spur mark.

77
JAR
Floral and butterfly designs in overglaze enamels
Arita ware, early Kakiemon style
3rd quarter 17th century
Height: 21.9 cm. Diameter: 22.0 cm. Foot: 11.5 cm.
Los Angeles County Museum of Art
63.16.3

Like the preceding example, this jar is somewhat atypical in its design. While the floral forms, rock and butterflies are common, the intrusion into the body of the cloud forms, the rectangular area of diaper pattern with its pendant forms

and architectural elements in the design give it a unique character. The colored enamels are the same as those in Dr. Stern's jar but their ap-pearance is very different because of the openness of the design and the great restraint used in the application of the black and red colors. The body and glaze are comparable in both examples. Each of these vessels is presumed to date slightly earlier than the jar from the Royal Ontario Museum. The significant differences in body and glaze as well as design would indicate a different site of manufacture or date between these jars and the Royal Ontario example.

FORMER COLLECTION: Nathan Hammer

78
KENDI
Lion and flowers in overglaze enamels
Arita export ware
2nd half 17th century
Height: 20.2 cm. Width: 7.5 cm. Foot: 8.3 cm.
The Art Gallery of Greater Victoria,
Fred and Isabel Pollard Collection
65:50

The body of this *kendi* is vigorously decorated in a landscape with peony and other floral forms rising from ground and rock forms with a not-so-ferocious leaping lion *(shi-shi)*. Floral forms decorate the flanged lip, stylized Dutch tulips decorate the neck, and sketchy cloud forms sur-round the spout. Around the base of the neck, a geometric design is contained between paired lines. The decoration is painted in blue, light green, red and black enamels. The *kendi* or gorge-let, as it was referred to in the *Registers* of the Dutch East India Company after the Portugese *gorgoletta*, is a drinking vessel whose shape seems to have been derived from a South Asian pottery shape. The *kendi* was a major commodity in the Chinese trade with the Indonesian Archipelago, the Malayan peninsula, and the Near East dur-ing the Ming period. The Japanese began pro-ducing the form to fill the need during the period when the civil strife in China cut off the production of export wares from Ching te Chen. After the introduction of tobacco to the Near

East, the *kendi* with the modification of wood or metal mountings became the popular body of the hookah. Both Chinese and Japanese examples of this modified form may still be found in the Near East along with the legion of modified shapes in metal, pottery and glass. The Japanese form is characterized by a large, flanged lip and a more slender neck than the Chinese model. Many of the Arita *kendi* have a smooth, globular body rather than the more flattened, molded body of the Chinese wares. However, one must look to the paste and peculiarities of the decoration to be certain of the origin as there was surely much inter-copying between the two areas. A fairly early date is tendered for both this and the other *kendi* in the exhibition (cat. no. 79) on the basis of the limited color scheme, the painting of which—particularly in this example—is more reminiscent of the blue and white ware of Sarugawa and related kilns than of mature enamel painting. The geometric border on the base of the neck and the broad bands of red enamel are also associated with the early Arita wares that are often described as Ko-Kutani style. Most of the *kendi* modeled and painted in this style have been described as Kakiemon style or type. Both the Victoria and Baltimore examples are related to the *kendi* in Roger Gerry's collection (See ref. 5, p. 50, pl. 16) which has characteristics of both vessels. Captain Gerry dates his *kendi* about 1670 which would also apply to the other two vessels. While this date is prudent, it is suggested that a dating preceding it by perhaps ten years is not out of the question.

79
KENDI
Landscape design in overglaze enamels
Arita export ware
2nd half 17th century
Height: 15.9 cm. Width: 11.9 cm. Foot: 6.3 cm.
The Baltimore Museum of Art
Gift of Mr. and Mrs. Lester S. Levy
55:182

Although of similar construction to the preceding example, this *kendi* is narrower of diameter and of less globular shape. The neck is longer and slimmer; the whole body tends, therefore, to appear more bottle-shaped. The neck is decorated with tulip design, the spout with cloud forms and the structural and design elements are separated with fairly broad lines of overglaze red. The principal design is a true landscape and is placed quite high on the body. Mountains, rocks, trees, water, boats, willows and plover are all represented by rapid outlines and thick washes of enamel colors in blue-green, blue and matte cherry red. The landscape design is remarkably similar to that found on Dr. Stern's jar (cat. no. 80).

80
JAR
Landscape in overglaze enamels
Arita ware, Early Kakiemon type
2nd half 17th century
Height: 28.0 cm. Diameter: 23.0 cm. Foot: 11.6 cm.
Dr. Harold P. Stern

The Kakiemon style even in its early stages is usually characterized by floral forms placed asymmetrically against a background that is left with generous open space. In this large and unusual example the body is decorated with a continuous landscape scene which occupies almost the entire surface of the vessel. The landscape design's relationship to contemporary painting and, in some respects to blue and white wares, is obvious. The color scheme of red, blue, green, yellow and linear black is carefully composed for both effect and realism as is the design itself. These enamel colors are all applied thickly over the uniformly crackled glaze. The decoration on the neck, shoulder, and lower portion of the jar is limited to simple lines, bands of color, and uncomplicated repeating design. While the design is atypical, the color scheme, the handling of the enamel color, the body and the glaze would place the piece among the earliest examples decorated in overglaze enamels.

81

BOTTLE
Tree peonies and rocks in overglaze enamels
Arita export ware, Kakiemon type
Last half 17th century
Height: 28.0 cm. Diameter: 8.9 cm. Foot: 8.2 cm.
Center of Asian Art and Culture,
The Avery Brundage Collection,
M. H. de Young Memorial Museum
B62 P21

This bottle in a European shape is decorated in pale overglaze red, blue, turquoise, ochre and aubergine on a warm white, pitted glaze. The bottom is unglazed. The simple, clean lines of this mundane form have been used to great advantage by the decorator. Rising from the mass of the rock forms, the recurving peony branch provides a pattern of motion on the form. The open peony blooms are strategically placed on the hip of the bottle, and the orchid leaves, repeating the lines of the bottle's shape, add lightness and an elegant upward motion to the composition. Outline is used sparingly and the color scheme is consistently understated in the economical use of hue and in its generally pale character. The strong composition never dominates the simple form but rather enriches it. In addition, the rich blue mouthpiece of the bottle provides a charming foil for the strength of the design. The top or mouthpiece has two small indentations opposite one another which probably served to hold some sort of closure apparatus. I have not been able to find the exact prototype of this bottle including the holes in the mouthpiece, but it is doubtless European and probably Dutch.

82

JAR
Autumn flowers and grasses in overglaze enamels
Arita ware, early Kakiemon type
2nd half 17th century
Height: 19.7 cm. Diameter: 16.5 cm. Foot: 9.8 cm.
The Royal Ontario Museum
959.150

Jars of similar form and decoration apparently found favor both in Europe and in Japan as examples have been noted in both areas prior to the recent mobility of Japanese art objects between East and West. A jar of nearly identical size and design is in the collection of the Museum of Fine Arts, Boston, and a similar jar with a lid is part of The Avery Brundage Collection in San Francisco. Other variations of the form are in the Munsterberg Collection and in the Hans Syz Collection of the Smithsonian Institution (See ref. 36, p. 670). A less sophisticated example than any of the foregoing, and one which may have been the prototype of this whole class of vessels, is in the Tokyo National Museum. This jar was shown in the Oakland Exhibition in 1961 and published in its catalogue as one of the very earliest of the Kakiemon wares. Distinctive variations of design, enamel colors and their renderings as well as the more subtle differences of shape and potting might, through analysis, yield a sequential dating for these beautiful early examples of the Kakiemon style. Of the relatively large group of similarly designed jars, the Toronto jar here illustrated is among the most handsome. The design concept is simple, and the rendering is accomplished and spirited.

PUBLISHED: Jenyns, Soame. *Japanese Porcelain.* New York: Frederick A. Praeger, 1965, p. 54 (as belonging to Mayuyama).

Mayuyama, Junkichi. *Japanese Art in the West.* Tokyo: Mayuyama and Company, 1966, p. 310, pl. 383.

Heinrich, Theodore Allen. *Art Treasures in the Royal Ontario Museum.* Toronto: McClelland Stewart, Ltd., 1963.

83

MODEL OF A BEAUTY
Overglaze enamels
Arita ware, Kakiemon type
Late 17th century
Height: 37.9 cm.
The Cleveland Museum of Art,
John L. Severance Fund
64.366

The superb quality and flawless condition of this figure make it outstanding among known

Kakiemon molded wares. The richness of design and brilliance of enamels reflect not only the Kakiemon style at a high point in its development but also the taste of the flamboyant Genroku period itself. The Genroku taste in costume was bright, gay, rich, often gaudy, and in constant conflict with the sumptuary laws. The underkimono is decorated with an allover design of *shippo tsunagi,* the interlacing of the cash design seen so often on the backs of Nabeshima wares. This design is painted in a rich iron red. The overkimono, *uchikake* or *kaidori,* is decorated with a design of weeping cherry blossoms in red and yellow with turquoise and green leaves and touches of black. The brilliant and elegant design beautifully accentuates the sweeping fall of the garment. The *obi* and hair are painted in a rich, shiny, lacquer-like black enamel. The large and stately figure is molded quite thinly and is finished with fine care. Three figures of similar scale and design are reproduced and discussed by Jenyns (See ref. 14, pl. 63B). The figure is reproduced in color in the *Bulletin of the Cleveland Museum* (See below).

PUBLISHED: Lerner, Martin. "Tea-Ceremony Pottery and Export Porcelain," *The Bulletin of the Cleveland Museum of Art,* Vol. LIV, No. 9 (November, 1967), back cover.

Mayuyama, Junkichi. *Japanese Art in the West.* Tokyo: Mayuyama and Company, 1966, p. 398.

84
TEAPOT
Floral decoration in overglaze enamels
Arita Ware, Kakiemon type
Last quarter 17th century
Height: 16.1 cm. Width: 20.4 cm. Foot: 7.2 cm.
Mrs. George H. Bunting, Jr.

This teapot is decorated in typical Kakiemon enamels and is representative of the type of pot which was probably exported in some quantity during the third quarter of the 17th century. While the precise origin for the shape of this particular type is not known, it is presumably derived from a European form which in turn was derived from the Chinese *Yi-Hsing* teapots known to have been exported to Europe. Examples of *Yi-Hsing* wares in molded gourd forms bearing some resemblance to this pot are known. The flattened panels of the side of the pot are a most expedient way of rendering on a rounded form the vertical floral designs popular on the flat-sided vessels of the period. Although somewhat stylized, the design of the floral forms is essentially quite realistic in rendering and particularly in placement. The designs are quickly, almost casually, painted in brilliant enamels. The spontaneous quality of the painting and design of many of these early wares is often their charm. All too frequently, the later wares were too meticulously designed and painted and lacked the qualities of vitality and spontaneity found here. Jenyns dates a similar pot as probably the Empo-Jokyo era (1673-1687) (See ref. 14, pl. 78a). The spout of the vessel has been repaired.

85
WINE EWER
Floral and phoenix in overglaze enamels
Arita ware, Kakiemon type
1st half 18th century
Width: 19.0 cm. Height: 15.9 cm. Foot: 8.9 cm.
Center of Asian Art and Culture,
The Avery Brundage Collection,
M. H. de Young Memorial Museum
B65 P59

The unusual form of this vessel is probably related to the *kendi* form, modified with the addition of the spout and a handle to make it highly functional as a sake pot. The funnel-like opening at the top allows wine to be poured in at any time with little chance of spilling and yet provides a narrow opening for the least escape of heat. The thick, high, curving handle allows easy pouring and good protection from the heat of the pot. The vessel is decorated with a limited color scheme of overglaze blue, yellow and red with outlines in black. The decoration on the body of the pot consists of peonies with floral scrolling arabesques. The shoulder is informally decorated with phoenix and cloud forms above a repeating stylized floral border. The cup-shaped opening at the top is decorated with five cash and both handle and spout have simple floral scrolling. The base is potted with a short foot similar to that of a jar or bottle.

86

JUG OR EWER

Birds and flowers in overglaze enamels
Arita ware, Kakiemon type
Last quarter 17th century
Height: 21.6 cm. Diameter: 11.4 cm. Foot: 7.5 cm.
Honolulu Academy of Arts
3532.1

The shape of this vessel is a more sophisticated version of the earlier blue and white export form derived from Dutch models. The design of birds and flowers is painted in blue, yellow, green and red. While not typical in either design or color scheme of the Kakiemon style, it is very closely related to it. The almost arabesque form of the floral pattern is related to the late 17th century Kakiemon wares as is the vertical tulip-like design on the neck. Volker published a more typical example of the same color scheme and size in his later book (See ref. 39, pl. II, no. 2). Jenyns publishes a nearly identical piece from the Reitlinger Collection in *Japanese Porcelain* (See ref. 14, pl. 38Aii). The handle has been pierced at the top for the attachment of a metal lid.

87

DISH

Birds and flowers in overglaze enamels
Arita ware, Kakiemon type
2nd half 17th century
Diameter: 31.6 cm. Height: 5.0 cm. Foot: 14.7 cm.
The Cleveland Museum of Art,
The Cornelia Blakemore Warner Fund
62.40

This is a good example of the formative phase of the Kakiemon style. The spontaneity of the drawing within the structural framework of the design gives these wares a personal quality that is often missing in the later export wares. The design is painted in iron red, pale green, blue, turquoise and a pale ochre yellow. The warmth of the color scheme is intensified by the buff-toned appearance of the rather thin glaze over the greyed body. The glaze shows some iridescence on the interior. The dish is potted in the helmet shape and with exceptional thinness for its size. The back of the dish is undecorated, but the base shows four spur marks, one central with three others triangulated about it. The foot is short and quite thin. The body, glaze and enamel colors are comparable to the Royal Ontario Museum jar (cat. no. 82).

88

LARGE DISH

Floral design in overglaze enamels
Arita export ware, Kakiemon type
2nd half 17th century
Diameter: 31.4 cm. Height: 5.4 cm. Foot: 16.0 cm.
The Metropolitan Museum of Art,
Gift of Mr. and Mrs. H. G. Wathen, 1966
66.118.1

This fairly heavily potted helmet shape dish is painted with rich red, turquoise, sapphire blue, and yellow over a carefully drawn black outline. Three spurs still adhere to the base of the short, sandy triangular foot. The exterior is undecorated. The vigor of painting and design of the "three friends" motif around the central reserve of this dish is of considerable interest. This design not only surrounds the central decoration but also provides a counter-clockwise motion that draws the eye always back to the central rock form and its exotic floral forms. The colors are harmonious and satisfying against the warm, milky white of the ground. The body is not exceptional in its potting and the glaze is unevenly applied, pitted and dirty. The handsomeness of the overall effect and the compelling quality of the design overcome these defects and attest to the high level of artistry of the Arita craftsmen.

89

BOTTLE

Birds, rocks and flowers in overglaze enamels
Arita ware, Kakiemon type
Last quarter 17th century
Height: 40.4 cm. Diameter: 21.8 cm. Foot: 13.4 cm.
Mr. and Mrs. John D. Rockefeller 3rd

The size, shape and decoration of this bottle all combine to make it a true masterwork of the Kakiemon style. The strength of the design and the brilliance of the colored enamels are admirably suited to the sturdy elegance of the shape. The broad washes of color in the rock areas form an ideal support for the birds silhouetted against the cool white of the body and serve to stabilize the composition. The sweeping forms of chrysanthemums and leaves add vigor and decorative interest. While probably an export piece, the bottle is totally Japanese in feeling and rises above so many of the export wares in terms of its strength of form and design and in its avoidance of the all too often found prettiness in Kakiemon wares. A bottle of similar design and shape is illustrated in *Sekai Toki Zenshu,* Vol. 4, color pl. 14 (See ref. 34).

90

OCTAGONAL BOWL

Plum, dragon and birds in overglaze enamels
Arita ware, Kakiemon type
Late 17th–early 18th century
Diameter: 25.5 cm. Height: 11.2 cm. Foot: 11.4 cm.
City Art Museum of Saint Louis
49:1970

A long-tailed *hoho* bird perched on a flowering plum branch with rocks and bamboo forms the main decoration of the outside of the bowl which has been left white except for another exotic bird in flight seen on the opposite side. The designs are painted with clear washes of pale yellow, turquoise, blue and iron red with black outline. Contrasting with this simple, descriptive decoration is the design of the interior which

has been formally planned and painted with a color scheme whose emphasis is predominately red. Evenly spaced alternate designs of three dragon medallions and three plum branches ring the sides of the bowl, and a paired *hoho* medallion is centered in the bottom. The iron red is used for most of the outlining of the forms, and the colored enamels are used very sparingly and then kept to their lightest hue. Black outline is applied only to those parts of the designs that carry strong motive line. The dragon medallions are particularly effective in their coloration. The red outline with the touches of blue on the scales gives the impression of an overall pale blue-violet hue. The precision of painting and impeccable design and color sense of the maker combined with the fine form and milk white purity of the body make this truly a masterpiece of the later Kakiemon style. The bowl has a flat brown rim, a high straight foot, and shows one tiny spur mark in the base.

91

LARGE BOWL

Multiple motives in overglaze enamels
Arita ware, Kakiemon type
Late 17th–early 18th century
Diameter: 32.8 cm. Height: 14.0 cm. Foot: 14.0 cm.
Mr. and Mrs. John D. Rockefeller 3rd

This very handsome bowl is a *tour de force* of Kakiemon enamel painting. The outside wall of the bowl is quietly decorated with large tree peony sprays in typical Kakiemon enamels. The underlip and foot as well as much of the side wall are left free of decoration. By contrast, the interior of the bowl seethes with activity. Around a dragon *mon* in the center of the bottom are ranged rockwork, banded hedge designs, plum, bamboo, various other floral forms and a wonderfully drawn tiger. The flowers and bamboo forms thrust their forms out into space in jutting, recurving and sweeping motions that give great energy to the design. Bamboo leaves, ends of branches and leaves, and even the tiger's extremely long tail, reach up the wall of the dish into the cavettoed brim as though the dish were unable to contain the strong activity. It is interesting to see those forms, which in so many examples of Kakiemon decoration are used to create a composition of perfect asymetrical balance, used here to produce such a vibrant atmosphere so full of motion. Physically, the bowl is constructed of a fine, clean white paste and is quite heavy. The high foot is square in section and sturdily made. The piece has an incised Johanneum mark in the base.

92

COVERED BOWL
Incised design, overglaze enamels and gold
Arita ware, Kakiemon type
Early 18th century
Diameter: 21.0 cm. Height: 14.5 cm. Foot: 11.1 cm.
The Cleveland Museum of Art,
James Parmelee Fund
61.42

This Kakiemon bowl represents the Kakiemon style at its apex. The refinement of taste and level of craftsmanship are unmatched. Over an incised and modeled design of waves, chrysanthemum flowers, leaves and plover *(chidori)* are painted in light iron red, brilliant blue and turquoise with a sparing use of gold. The pale, bluish-green glaze is apparent in the incised lines of the waves. The black outline is used to define the turquoise and blue leaves but the other forms are outlined exclusively in red. The carefully modeled strap handle is painted with a simple flower and leaf form in gold and red. The interior of the lid is decorated by a simple and elegant plum branch with leaves and flowers in the same colors but with an extensive use of black outlining. The bottom of the interior is painted with a large and brilliant design of two *hoho* in blue with red and gold tail feathers and two flaming pearl designs. The porcelain and its glaze are virtually flawless. The foot is high and sturdily made; the base has one small central spur mark. One other bowl of this type is known in this country. A similar example, but with different interior design, is illustrated in *Japanese Ceramics* (See ref. 29, pl. 78).

PUBLISHED: Mayuyama, Junkichi, *Japanese Art in the West.* Tokyo: Mayuyama and Company, 1966, p. 388.

Lee, Sherman E. *The Japanese Decorative Style.* Cleveland: The Cleveland Museum of Art, 1961, no. 147.

93

OCTAGONAL BOWL
Decorated with overglaze enamels
Arita ware, Kakiemon type
19th century
Diameter: 20.3 cm. Height: 10.2 cm. Foot: 9.5 cm.
The Metropolitan Museum of Art,
Gift of Mrs. V. Everit Macy, 1923
23.225.322

This is a particularly well painted example of the very late Kakiemon style which also shows the persistence of the octagonal shape as a desirable form. The bowl is decorated with three designs of *daikon,* Japanese radish, in clean, brilliant blue, green, yellow and red enamels. The only other design present is of two insects in iron red to disguise an imperfection in the body. The enamels are most carefully applied to delineate the forms which are meticulously outlined in black. The enamels and glaze have a quality of softness which one does not find in earlier Kakiemon wares. The bowl is nearly the same size as the undecorated bowl in the exhibition but differs in its molding, foot, paste and glaze. True to the form, the base shows one slightly off-center spur mark. It is precisely because of pieces of this nature that we cannot dismiss the 19th century wares as being of no interest.

PUBLISHED: James, F. S. *Macy Collection.* New York: c. 1896, no. 202.

FORMER COLLECTION: V. Everit Macy.

94

OCTAGONAL BOWL
Molded design and overglaze enamels
Arita ware, Kakiemon type
Early 18th century
Diameter: 18.9 cm. Height: 9.2 cm. Foot: 8.7 cm.
Philadelphia Museum of Art,
George W. B. Taylor Fund
58-118-1

The charming and descriptive decoration of this bowl shows an old woodsman who has dropped his hat, flowers, a long stick and scythe to chase a red dog who in turn is chasing a blue deer with green legs and yellow spots. The woodsman is dressed in brilliant blue. The foregoing scene is painted in rich enamels with a sketchily drawn, black outline. The interior of the bowl is beautifully molded in low relief. The eight panels are paired into views of bamboo and rock, plum blossoms, dragon and clouds, and a tiger in a landscape. Several enamel painted maple leaves are scattered in the bottom of the bowl. This vessel is constructed differently from the other octagonal bowls in the exhibition. It does not have the typical flanged lip rim, the angles of the sides are rounded softly, and the quite small footrim is rounded on the bottom rather than being square in section. It does carry the single, central spur on the flat base that is common to these vessels.

FORMER COLLECTIONS: Mrs. P. L. M. Tonbridge; and Karl Kempe.

95

OCTAGONAL BOWL
Undecorated
Arita ware, Kakiemon type
Early 18th century
Diameter: 21.4 cm. Height: 10.4 cm. Foot: 9.9 cm.
Philadelphia Museum of Art,
Gift of Mrs. Van Horn Ely
65-68-1

Kakiemon wares are not often found undecorated as most of the exported pieces were either enameled at Arita or, if shipped "in the white," rarely escaped the hand of the European enameler. If one looks to the taste of the eighteenth century with its passionate fascination with the decorated object, the comparative lack of white wares is not unexpected. In ceramic terms the appreciation of the pristine whiteness and the architectonic form enriched only by the austere, flat, brown lip rim is the taste of the twentieth century. This particular example is meaningful with regard to other decorated examples of the same shape. The form is particularly satisfying in itself, thus providing the decorator with a challenge which was so often well met, as witnessed by the surviving examples of the form. Physically, the bowl is finely crafted of clean white paste. The foot is fairly high and square in section. A single, small spur mark is to be seen in the center of the base. It is presumed that the vessel was made sometime toward the end of the Kyoho era.

96

DISH IN CHRYSANTHEMUM SHAPE
Tiger and bamboo in overglaze enamels
Arita ware, Kakiemon type
Late 17th–early 18th century
Diameter: 15.3 cm. Height: 3.5 cm. Foot: 9.0 cm.
Philadelphia Museum of Art,
George W. B. Taylor Fund
55-10-3

The tiger and bamboo with the so-called banded hedge design is well known as it was frequently copied at Meissen and other European and English factories in the 18th century. The decoration is dominated by the form of the tiger which is painted in shades of iron red. The hedges are painted in black, but otherwise black is used very sparingly in the drawing. Ochre yellow, blue, green and some gold are all used sparingly. The dish is carefully made of fine white paste and the crenated rim is finished with an inside bevel cut. The flat base has one small spur mark in the center. Unfortunately, there has been some enamel loss through wear, however, this dish remains one of the finest examples of this type of Kakiemon ware in American collections.

97

CHRYSANTHEMUM-SHAPED BOWL
Floral design in overglaze enamels
Kakiemon ware
Last quarter 17th century
Diameter: 18.7 cm. Height: 8.6 cm. Foot: 8.3 cm.
The Baltimore Museum of Art
59.72

The first mention of exporting bowls of this shape is referred to by Volker (See ref. 39, p. 67 and illus. 7) in his survey of the Company records for the year 1684. The shape is referred to as a shell bowl—a perfectly obvious reading of the shape to European eyes accustomed to the ubiquitous scallop shell form. Although the bowl Volker mentions is probably decorated in the Imari style, the evidence of shape would seem to be accurate in terms of the Baltimore bowl and the bowl Mr. Volker illustrates in the same reference. It is presumed on the basis of the design that this bowl is a bit earlier. The purity of the design of the shape coupled with beautiful craftsmanship and the clean milky white body make these bowls particularly satisfying. The usually simple floral decoration of the outside does not intrude unduly upon the basic design but adds color and interest. The design here is presumably that of bellflowers, but its strict verticality is reminiscent of the often seen and highly appreciated tulip motif. A more freely drawn floral group decorates the opposite side. Two lone butterflies are placed in the undecorated spaces between the major designs. A peony spray in enamel colors is placed at the bottom of the interior of the bowl. There is a small spur mark in the center of the flat base.

98
VASE
Scattered designs in overglaze enamels and gold
Arita ware, Kakiemon type
Late 17th century
Height: 26.7 cm. Diameter: 21.0 cm. Foot: 12.0 cm.
Mr. and Mrs. Severance A. Millikin, Courtesy of
The Cleveland Museum of Art

The informally scattered design of floral sprigs, insects, lion, Chinese figure, pine tree and birds give a lighthearted charm to this elegant but sturdy form. The designs are painted in brilliant, clean Kakiemon colors with slight touches of gold. No particular color dominates. The vessel is wheel-potted of fine, hard, white paste. The chrysanthemum petal design on the shoulder and the compatible vertical modelings on the body are tool-worked and not molded. The glaze is quite green and bubbly especially in the intersticies of the modeling, giving the appearance of even greater third dimension. The soft quality produced by the modeling and glaze makes an excellent ground for the type of decoration used. Wares of this type greatly influenced European and English porcelains of the 18th century. The charm of the scattered decoration was appreciated of itself and its ability to "set off" and enhance the purity and whiteness of the porcelain was a quality much to be desired at the time. There was also a very practical reason for its ready acceptance. An overglaze enamel insect, flower or other small device could be used to conceal imperfection in an otherwise pristine piece. The porcelain painter's design skill was often tested when an untried composition presented itself based on the random defects acquired in the firing. This use of defects may be seen on later 17th and 18th century Japanese wares, but it was not so extensively used as on the less perfect Western wares where some very exotic compositions sometimes happened. In this jar the placement of the enamel painting is either dictated by the whim or design of the painter as the body and glaze are without objectionable flaws.

99
DEEP BOWL
Pine, plum and bamboo in overglaze enamels
Arita ware, Kakiemon type
Late 17th–early 18th century
Diameter: 34.3 cm. Height: 13.0 cm. Foot: 17.2 cm.
Mr. and Mrs. John D. Rockefeller 3rd

The interior of this large and handsome bowl is decorated with a series of pine, plum and bamboo motives with rockwork and birds in the typical Kakiemon palette found in wares of the period. Despite the freely drawn designs on the interior, the shape of the vessel combined with the exterior decoration and the interior border give it a rather formal appearance. Just below the beading at the top of the bowl, finely drawn and washed interlacing cash make a scallop-like border. The outside decoration is the familiar peony with leafy scrollwork but it is here quite stiffly formed into a formal arabesque-like design. This device became quite popular in Kakiemon and Imari wares and is seen quite often in the blue and white Imari bowls of the 18th century. The bowl is finely potted with a short, tapering footrim. The Cleveland Museum has in its collection a pair of bowls of almost identical size and design.

100
CHRYSANTHEMUM-SHAPED BOWL
Decorated with overglaze enamels
Arita ware, Kakiemon type
Late 17th–early 18th century
Diameter: 21.8 cm. Height: 7.6 cm. Foot: 11.0 cm.
Eugene Fuller Memorial collection,
Seattle Art Museum
69.J27.76

The rich decorative nature of the design of this piece is associated with the Shibuemon style. The apparent casualness of the design and color scheme is misleading. The elements of the design are most carefully placed and colored to achieve optimum effect. This interior design consists of five *kiri-mon,* or chrysanthemum crests, placed alternately with paulownia designs. A *hoho* bird with long, curving tail feathers is placed in the center. The colors used are a pale iron red-orange, yellow, blue, turquoise and black. The outside of the bowl is decorated with two groups of rockwork with plum and bamboo in the same palette. The glaze is thin and runs quite greenish in the depressions of the molded form. Its general appearance is a warm, soft milky white. The high, slightly sloping foot is flat on the bottom as is the unmarked, glazed base. The bowl accumulated some kiln dirt in the interior in the fir-

ing. The sixteen-petal chrysanthemum crest and the multiflowered paulownia suggest that this bowl might have been made for someone with Imperial connections or as an Imperial gift.

101
LOBED DISH
Underglaze blue with overglaze enamels
Arita ware, Kakiemon type
Early 18th century
Diameter: 18.0 cm. Height: 3.5 cm. Foot: 11.7 cm.
Mrs. George G. R. Harris

The rim and interior sides of this dish are molded in an eight-section lotiform shape. The design of a bird perched on bamboo stalk with rocks and plum is painted in underglaze blue with overglaze enamels. Rich red, yellow and somewhat opaque green enamel colors with extensive black outlining form the color scheme, the one exception being the bamboo section at the lower left enameled in a thick, dark aubergine. The back is decorated with two opposing designs of a bird on a flowering branch. A "running" *fuku* mark in a double square is centered on the base which has three spur marks. The short, triangular foot is very thinly formed at the bottom. This design was apparently quite popular as there are a number of known examples with the same design scheme and shape, most of which, however, are inferior in design and rendering and may be of later date. The enamels used here are quite a bit brighter than the earlier Kakiemon type enamels. The red in particular is of a deeper hue and less orange than one expects of Kakiemon of the 17th century. It is of interest to note with regard to the enamels that they have degraded or hazed the glaze in the firing in the same manner one is accustomed to seeing on early 18th century Nabeshima wares. Apparently, some of the enamels used by several of the decorating establishments were constituted in a new and different manner than those of the earlier period. The possibility of this piece being a Nabeshima product is remote, as is borne out by the quality and color of the glaze as well as the design.

102

EIGHT-LOBED PLATE
Pine, plum and bamboo in overglaze enamels
Arita ware, Kakiemon type
Late 17th–early 18th century
Diameter: 18.8 cm. Height: 2.8 cm. Foot: 13.4 cm.
Eugene Fuller Memorial Collection,
Seattle Art Museum
59.J27.47

The "three friends" design with rocks and birds decoration is painted in a rich variegated blue, a pale clear yellow, turquoise, green, iron red, black and touches of gold with a brown edge. The design is essentially that found on a pair of plates with the addition of banded hedges published by Jenyns (See ref. 14, 77A and B). This pair is of particular interest because the second is an early 18th century copy of the design by a Dutch enameler on a Chinese body. Mr. Jenyns dates the Japanese version: "about 1700." The Seattle example is a fine one of its type. The plate is finely finished and the design nicely composed and beautifully painted. The glaze is thin and clean and slightly matte on the inside. The base shows five small, carefully placed spur marks. The foot is short and triangular.

PUBLISHED: *Japanese Art in the Seattle Art Museum.* Seattle Art Museum, 1960, no. 156.

EXHIBITED: San Francisco, M. H. de Young Memorial Museum, *Treasures of Japan,* 1960.

Seattle Art Museum, *Japanese Art in the Seattle Museum,* 1960.

103

EIGHT-LOBED DISH
Butterfly design in overglaze enamels
Arita ware, Kakiemon type
Early 18th century
Diameter: 21.6 cm. Height: 3.5 cm. Foot: 13.5 cm.
Mrs. George H. Bunting, Jr.

This fascinating 18th century Japanese design would probably find ready acceptance among the youthful devotees of psychedelic art. I think we may presume, though, that the originator of the design was enraptured by nothing more than the sight of butterflies flitting about a spider web still covered with the early dew and sparkling in the morning light. The rendering of the theme, however mundane, is both ingenious and highly successful in the result. The color scheme is simple and consists of brilliant enamel colors in blue, yellow, iron red and a lacquer-like black. Just below the brown, beaded lip is a molded rope design which encircles the dish. The exterior is undecorated. The foot is short and triangular in section and the base shows five tiny spur marks. The appearance of the glaze is a soft, milky white and the body is clean, hard and white.

104

SIX-LOBED BOWL
Double phoenix design in overglaze enamels
Arita ware, Kakiemon type
Early 18th century
Diameter: 24.6 cm. Height: 4.6 cm. Foot: 14.2 cm.
Mrs. George H. Bunting, Jr.

This bowl is somewhat unusually shaped. The finely potted side walls have been pinched in to form six slightly incurving lobes. Also unusual is the short, splayed foot applied to the bottom. Although other bowls of this size and conformation are known, the technique of production does not seem to have spread to other wares. The design of two *hoho* birds with their extraordinarily long tail feathers is very artfully fitted to the form. It is painted in blue, blue-green, a brilliant yellow, aubergine with black, and iron red. The back of the bowl is sparingly decorated with seven paulownia clusters carefully placed in a "random" pattern. Both interior and exterior designs are carefully thought out in terms of the shape on which they are applied and in the relationship of enamel colors. The pristine, milky-white, smooth surface of the vessel enhances the spaciousness of the elegant design.

105

SQUARE BOTTLE
Pine, plum and bamboo in overglaze enamels
Arita ware, Kakiemon type
Late 17th–early 18th century
Height: 22.5 cm. Width: 10.1 cm. Foot: 9.0 cm.
The Newark Museum, Gift of N. V. Hammer
J.67.108

The design of this bottle is painted in a rich opaque grey-blue, green, iron red, brown, yellow, pink and black with touches of gold. The painting is meticulously ordered to take advantage of the entire palette used. Imperfections in the glaze are also effectively incorporated into the design. The design of the bottle itself is carefully thought out. The flat sides of the vessel slope inward slightly to give a light, graceful appearance. The gentle curve to the shoulder angles and the soft finishing of the edges contribute, along with the finesse of the decoration, to produce an especially satisfying object of some elegance. The range and quality of colors used indicate that this bottle was produced shortly before the turn of the century, if not in the early years of the 18th century.

106

LOBED BOWL
Designs in underglaze blue and overglaze enamels
Arita ware, Kakiemon type
Early 18th century
Diameter: 25.4 cm. Height: 14.0 cm. Foot: 13.6 cm.
The Mr. and Mrs. Severance A. Millikin Collection,
Courtesy of the Cleveland Museum of Art

The everted rim of the bowl is formed into eight flattened lobes and finished with a flat brown edge. From each notch in the rim the body has a raised, molded element that swirls toward the bottom of the inside of the vessel. The exterior is decorated with rockwork, peony and bamboo in underglaze blue augmented by overglaze enamels in turquoise, yellow, red and black. In the case of some of the peony sprays the red enamel is painted over the underglaze blue. The interior bottom of the dish has a design of a leaping lion, *shishi,* and two ribboned cash in underglaze blue with red enamel whiskers. Each

lobe of the interior has a flower spray painted in red, yellow and turquoise with some black outline on the leaves. A repeating acanthus-like design in the same color scheme decorates the lower part of the bowl above the double blue lines enclosing the lion. The glaze which appears to be quite thin has a soft matte quality that greys and softens the effect of the underglaze blue. The high, slightly tapering foot is quite flat on the bottom. The base is marked "kin" in a double square within a broad circle. Three very tiny spur marks are apparent. The paste as shown at the foot is hard, fine and speckled with imperfections. The high quality of the design and color scheme of the enamel painting give this vessel particular importance. It is not known if the soft quality of the glaze was intentional or accidental.

PUBLISHED: Lee, Sherman E. *The Japanese Decorative Style.* Cleveland: The Cleveland Museum of Art, 1961, pl. 163, p. 130.

Jenyns, Soame. *Japanese Porcelain.* New York: Frederick A. Praeger, 1965, pl. 71.

107

SQUARE PLATE
Underglaze blue with overglaze enamels
Arita ware, Kakiemon type
Early 18th century
Width: 15.0 cm. Height: 3.3 cm. Foot: 11.3 cm.
Mr. and Mrs. Henry Trubner

These small dishes can be fairly securely dated to the first years of the 18th century by their appearance in the Dresden collection and the K'ang Hsi copies that replaced them in the trade. Jenyns illustrates a Japanese dish in the Reitlinger collection and a Chinese copy (See ref. 14, pl. 79). The design is of a cock and hen with a pair of dragons and a pair of designs of peony with leafy scrolling on the borders. Cloud forms are interspersed among both motives. Mr. and Mrs. Trubner have a nearly identical plate in their collection in which the positions of the dragon and floral motives are reversed. The exterior is decorated with simple floral scrollwork centered on each of the four sides. A stylized *fuku* mark is placed within a center square in the center of the base. There are four spur marks: one central and the other three triangulated about it. The form of the dish is a square with notched and molded corners. The lip rim is brown.

FORMER COLLECTION: The Norton Collection, London.

108
DISH
Floral design in underglaze blue with
overglaze enamels
Arita ware
Late 17th–early 18th century
Diameter: 18.5 cm. Height: 3.0 cm. Foot: 12.0 cm.
Mrs. George H. Bunting, Jr.

This uncommonly rich design of peony buds and flowers is carried out in overglaze enamels in a rich iron red, pale yellow and green complimented by a deep underglaze blue. The rendering of the underglaze blue has a soft and somewhat blurred appearance which enhances the brilliance of the overglaze colors, particularly the dominant red of the stylized peony, and helps to give the design its almost three dimensional quality. The exterior of the dish shows a very simple running floral and leaf design. The rather crudely painted, spurious Ch'eng Hua mark dominates the bottom of the dish. Three large, triangulated spur marks are centered on the bottom. The foot is short, triangular and unglazed on the bottom. Some kiln grit still adheres to the foot. The dating of this dish presents problems because of the unusual and conflicting aspects of the piece. It is certainly related to the Kakiemon wares in the use and colors of overglaze enamels and in the running scrolling on the back, yet the body potting and design scheme are not what one expects of Kakiemon export ware. The design seems to be closely related to a small dish of about the same size exhibited in the Oakland Exhibition (See ref. 15, no. 69, pl. 37) and attributed to the Himetani kiln and dated Early Edo period. It is not sug-

gested that the dish is of such early date or provenance, but it would tend to give more consideration to a 17th century date. The size and decoration would also indicate that the dish was made for the Japanese market and not for export. Three other almost identical dishes are now in American collections and all seem to have come from Japan. A fifth dish would make a set. Perhaps we are dealing here with the product of a small Arita kiln making wares for local consumption based on traditional needs and design schemes. There is certainly ample evidence of the continuing tradition of the elegantly painted Kakiemon blue and white wares of the early 18th century and those which use a combination of blue and white and enamels. Many of the small dishes of this type carry the running scrolling on the back, the Chinese reign marks, and retain the obviously useful form and size. The body, glaze, enamels, underglaze blue, indeed the general character of the dish, all suggest a reasonably early date rather than a later one. One of the dishes in American collections is in the Munsterberg Collection and was published by Professor Munsterberg as 18th century Imari ware in ref. 26, p. 247—an attribution not to be left unconsidered. The great charm of these particular dishes makes a search for truly comparable pieces and a sure provenance and date worth undertaking.

109
PAIR OF BOWLS
Underglaze blue and overglaze enamels
Arita ware, Kakiemon type
18th century
Diameter: 20.4 cm. Height: 5.5 cm. Foot: 14.4 cm.
The Detroit Institute of Arts,
Gift of Mr. and Mrs. Mark Littler
69.475 and .476

These bowls are flat bottomed with fairly thick walls and an everted lip. The decoration consists of two *hoho* birds painted in red, turquoise blue and yellow enamels on the bottom of the interior and, on the sides, a repeating row of precious jewels or cash in underglaze blue, below which six identical motives are repeated in enamels. The outside is decorated with a continuous open design of scroll work in underglaze blue. The base carries a poorly drawn, six-character Ch'eng Hua mark, also in underglaze blue. An interesting feature of these bowls is their apparent relationship to the Nabeshima wares of the period in the use of the cash motif and the degrading of the glaze around the overglaze enamels. It would seem that the use of the underglaze blue in combination with the enamels and motives was directly in emulation of the Nabeshima wares. The glaze and body are what one would expect of a Kyoho period Kakiemon piece. There are seven spur marks on the base, one central and six neatly circled about it.

FORMER COLLECTION: Milo Perkins

110
DEEP DISH
Underglaze blue and overglaze enamels
Arita ware, Kakiemon type
Late 17th–early 18th century
Diameter: 20.7 cm. Height: 4.8 cm. Foot: 8.6 cm.
City Art Museum of Saint Louis
1:62

This dish has been attributed to the style and time of Shibuemon on the basis of a dish with the same design in Japan that is marked on the base: "Kaki/Genroku twelfth year" or 1699 (See ref. 30, pp. 103, 104, figs. 249, 252). The ingeniously conceived design of brocade pattern and peony blossoms and buds with rope tendrils is painted in what is essentially a K'ang Hsi color scheme. Underglaze blue is used throughout with green, pale yellow, aubergine, rich iron red and black with some gold. The dish is heavily constructed at the bottom but becomes quite thin in the everted lip which is finished with a nearly straight, vertical lip. The base is flat and unmarked. The glaze is thick and glassy and has a decidedly blue-green appearance.

111
LOBED PLATE
Heron design in underglaze blue
Arita ware, Kakiemon type
Early 18th century
Diameter: 21.4 cm. Height: 3.1 cm. Foot: 13.3 cm.
City Art Museum of Saint Louis,
W. K. Bixby Oriental Art Trust Fund
32:69

Plates such as this one were often produced in sets of ten or twenty, a factor we are easily prone to forget when looking at the superior quality of the rendering. The decorators of these wares must have been master craftsmen of the highest sort to have turned out in quantity painting that is filled with vigor and sensitivity. The decoration here is of a heron, rock and water plants in the center. The eight-lobed brim is decorated with maple leaves and waves—a theme particularly beloved by the Nabeshima designers. It is interesting to compare this border decoration with that of the back of the Shibuemon style plate from Seattle (cat. no. 112). This design, the shape of the plate, and the double lines on the brim all point to a close relationship between these two pieces. The plate rests on a short, triangular foot. The base shows five tiny spur marks well placed around the center. The base is marked with a six-character *Ch'eng Hua nien ho* in blue.

112
LARGE, LOBED PLATE
Underglaze blue, overglaze enamels and gold
Arita ware, Shibuemon type
Late 17th–early 18th century
Diameter: 34.2 cm. Height: 4.7 cm. Foot: 21.7 cm.
Gift of Mrs. John C. Atwood, Jr.,
Seattle Art Museum
60.J27.63

The design here is of brocaded tressels and paulownia. In both design position and coloration the paulownia leaf and flower group within the double circle is the key to the design and holds added significance in that it becomes a *kiri-mon* or paulownia crest. The formal *kiri-mon* was used in differing forms by a number of leading families including the Imperial household. Considering the strictness with which the Imperial crest was allowed to be used, it would seem safe to say that the *mon* here used refers to some other noble family. It is of interest to compare this formalized design with the more naturalistic one seen on a Nabeshima plate illustrated in *Iro Nabeshima* (See ref. 27, black and white pl. 25). This plate has been attributed to the Kakiemon kilns when they were under the jurisdiction of Shibuemon because of a plate in Japan that is marked *"kaki"* with a Genroku date comparable to 1699 (See ref. 30, pp. 103, 104 and figs. 250 and 253). See also Jenyns (ref. 14, pl. 43c). Another unmarked plate of this kind is in the Freer Gallery of Art. Physically, the plate is constructed of fine white porcelain with rounded sides and everted lip finished with a short, vertical beading. The short, sloping foot is rounded. The bottom is flat and is marked with a central design of *daikon* within a broad circle. Eight spur marks are to be seen on the bottom.

113
PLATE

Shore scene in underglaze blue
Arita ware, Kakiemon type
Early 18th century
Diameter: 20.8 cm. Height: 3.7 cm. Foot: 14.2 cm.
Mrs. George H. Bunting, Jr.

This plate is very similar to the Seattle sweetfish plate (cat. no. 114), in size, shape, the design of the back with floral scrolling and *fuku* mark, and the characteristics of the body and foot. It differs from that plate in the complexity of the design scheme, which is a true landscape, and the rendering, which is of a more delicate nature. There are also some minor differences in the rendering and design of the floral scrolling on the back. Like the Seattle plate, the conception of this design is enlightened. The scene with drying fishnets is beautifully painted in a fine, clear underglaze blue. The strength of the design and quality of the painting of these early 18th century Kakiemon wares distinguish them from the too often artless but meticulously painted blue and white wares of the 19th century.

114
PLATE

Three fish design in underglaze blue
Arita ware, Kakiemon type
Early 18th century
Diameter: 22.2 cm. Height: 2.9 cm. Foot: 14.6 cm.
Eugene Fuller Memorial Collection,
Seattle Art Museum
64.J26.29

The theme of sweetfish (*ayu*) swimming is masterfully carried out in both the design and its rendering. The back of the plate is decorated with well painted running floral scrollwork. A "running" *fuku* mark within a double square is centered on the base of the plate within a broad circle. The foot rim is wide and the foot is short, triangular in section, and quite thin at the bottom. The base has four small spur marks. The potting is excellent and the glaze is good but minutely pocked on the interior. The lip rim is pale tobacco brown in color. There is an identical plate in the Avery Brundage Collection in San Francisco. Both plates are presumed to have come from a set of ten, eight of which are still in Japan. The set's box is inscribed with the former owner, Goto Koheiji, and the date "8th year of Hoei," or 1711 A.D. If this information is correct, and there is no reason to think otherwise, these plates are an important touchstone for the dating of early blue and white Kakiemon.

115
FOOTED DISH

Underglaze blue and overglaze enamels
Nabeshima ware, 1st half 18th century
Diameter: 15.3 cm. Height: 3.9 cm. Foot: 8.3 cm.
The University of Michigan Museum of Art,
Margaret Watson Parker Art Collection

This design of three storage jars is one of Nabeshima's most successful non-floral designs. The flattened outlines of the three identically sized jars are ranked one behind the other from right to left across the plate. A false sense of perspective is achieved through the placement and patterning of the vessel shapes. The vase in the foreground is outlined in underglaze blue with rich cherry red flower petals and blue-green leaves; the lower portion, or "unglazed" area is painted in a deep underglaze blue wash as is the mouth and outline. The middle crackle ware vase is rendered solely in underglaze blue. The remaining jar is outlined in blue and the "glazed" upper portion is decorated with a key-fret motif in red. The designs are set against a pale underglaze blue-washed background. The exterior of the dish is decorated with freely drawn and washed peony flowers and leafy scrolling in a tri-partite scheme. The foot has the usual comb pattern. The potting of this piece is quite heavy in the dish and the foot rim. It is presumed that this is an early example of Nabeshima ware. See Sister Johanna Becker's fine article on this and four other plates in the University's collection below.

PUBLISHED: Becker, Sister Johanna. "A Group of Nabeshima Porcelain," *The University of Michigan Museum of Art Bulletin,* Vol. III. Ann Arbor: 1968, p. 21, fig. 5; p. 25, fig. 9; p. 26, fig. 5.

116
MOLDED DISH
Underglaze blue and overglaze enamels
Nabeshima ware, 1st half 18th century
Length: 15.2 cm. Width: 12.1 cm. Height: 3.6 cm.
Honolulu Academy of Arts
3667.1

This dish is attractively molded in a scalloped, oblong form on a high foot. The shallow interior is decorated with a series of camellia flowers and leaves. The flower petals are left white with blue outline, the centers are a thick, deep yellow enamel, and the leaves are blue-green. The whole design is set against an allover key-fret pattern in underglaze blue. The thick enamels have extensively degraded the glaze about them to good effect, producing a matte surface on the camellia petals and imparting a soft, hazy quality to the underglaze blue about the leaves. The back is decorated with three designs of peony flower and leaves with floral scrolling in the *takokarakusa*

manner. The foot is decorated with a repeating design of wave-like forms in a band of washed underglazed blue. The high foot is quite thick and oval in shape. The form of the dish is related to, and perhaps directly influenced by, Matsugatani wares. It is presumed that this dish comes from the early period of Nabeshima production.

117
FOOTED DISH
Underglaze blue and overglaze enamels
Nabeshima ware, early 18th century
Diameter: 15.6 cm. Height: 3.4 cm. Foot: 8.1 cm.
City Art Museum of Saint Louis,
W. K. Bixby Oriental Art Trust Fund
142:59

Designs drawn from brocade patterns were apparently the first decorations used on the Iro-Nabeshima wares of the early 18th century. They are characterized by repeating medallion patterns taken from textile designs augmented by traditional ceramic decoration. The backs are usually decorated by a simple tri-partite peony design with leafy scrolling in a pale underglaze blue. The bodies are potted quite shallowly on a high foot. The *nishikide,* or comb pattern, is usually employed on the foot, but there are some examples with no decoration on the backs or foot. These earliest wares are also characterized by a glaze which is decidedly yellowish in appearance on the backs of the dishes. The overglaze enamels used in these wares are usually limited to three colors, and the effect is somewhat subdued by contrast with later examples. The design of this attractive, small dish is completely drawn and washed in underglaze blue with a subtle use of green and pale yellow and a dominant, dark, rich red enhanced by red overdrawing. Three other dishes from the same set are to be found in the collections of the Royal Ontario Museum, the Millikin Collection in the Cleveland Museum of Art and the Indianapolis Institute of Art. Other dishes with early brocade designs are rare in American collections.

118

FOOTED DISH
Underglaze blue and overglaze enamels
Nabeshima ware, early 18th century
Diameter: 15.1 cm. Height: 3.4 cm. Foot: 8.2 cm.
The Detroit Institute of Arts,
G. Albert Lyon Foundation
69.85

With the exception of some warpage in its body this dish is nearly identical with the St. Louis dish (cat. no. 117) in potting, size and underglaze blue decoration. However, the whole design concept is changed by the disposition of the overglaze enamels on the underglaze blue drawing. The green enamel dominates the decoration giving the design a richer and more somber appearance. So altered is the composition in color and design that it is difficult to compare the two renderings in terms of quality—each has its own strengths and weaknesses within the context of the enamel painter's intention. One wonders if this plate was not a part of the original set and purposefully decorated in this manner for its effect in juxtaposition with the remainder of the group. It is not an un-Japanese notion.

119

CUP WITH SILVER LINER
Underglaze blue and overglaze enamels
Nabeshima ware, 18th century
Diameter: 9.0 cm. Height: 5.5 cm. Foot: 3.9 cm.
Mrs. George H. Bunting, Jr.

In both shape and decoration this tea cup is an outstanding and unusual example of Nabeshima ware. The designs of flying *Apsaras* with musical instruments are silhouetted against underglaze blue. The figures are finely drawn in underglaze blue with delicately painted shades of yellow, pale green and a rich, dark red. The cup is very finely potted. It is not known whether the silver liner is contemporary with the bowl or is a later addition. The interior is undecorated. It is from wares of this quality that Nabeshima wares have gained the reputation of being the finest of Japanese porcelains.

120

SET OF FIVE MOLDED DISHES
Persimmon design in underglaze blue and overglaze enamels
Nabeshima ware, 18th century
Diameter: 10.0 cm. Height: 2.0 cm.
The Philadelphia Museum of Art,
Gift of Mrs. Herbert C. Morris
61-118-3-7

The design scheme of two persimmons with leaves is achieved through the molded shape of the dishes combined with underglaze blue and overglaze enamels. The central persimmon is painted in a shaded iron red, the calyx in tobacco brown, the other persimmon and three of the leaves in underglaze blue, and the remaining leaf in a brilliant green enamel over underglaze blue drawing. The outside of the high foot is decorated with a pine needle motif, and the back of the dish displays an interesting stylized linear scrolling—both of which are drawn in blue. The most striking aspect of these small dishes is the effect of the red persimmon in the composition, because the iron red or, as it is often called, persimmon red is handled in such a manner as to appear to the eye precisely as a ripe Japanese persimmon does. Overglaze red in large areas does not normally appear. Much of the effect has to do with the manner of mottling and shading of the color, but credit must go also to the use of the tobacco brown in the calyx and the juxtaposition of the red against the cool underglaze blues and emerald green enamels. In Nabeshima wares of this class, the interdependence of potting and design and the quality of both the underglaze and overglaze painting is critical. Where one of these essentials is lacking in quality, the pieces fail. I have handled other sets of this design which, while not without interest, are very little more than pretty pieces and cannot be measured against the truly precious—in the best sense of the term—quality of this set. The Philadelphia Museum records this as Genroku era, but I suggest that the earliest possible dating one could assign would be Kyoho (1716-1735), based on the potting and glaze.

121

FOOTED DISH

Underglaze blue and overglaze enamels
Nabeshima ware, 1st half 18th century
Diameter: 14.9 cm. Height: 4.4 cm. Foot: 8.2 cm.
Los Angeles County Museum of Art,
Gift of Harry Packard
63.39

The floral forms depicted here have been described as representing gentian flowers. I should think it much more likely that they are one of the seven flowers of autumn and probably thoroughwort, the Japanese *fujibakama*. Whatever the flowers' proper name may be, the design on this small dish is representative of the style and technique of the finest floral painting in the Nabeshima wares. The painting is sure and vigorous, but its technique does not dominate the composition. The underglaze blue and overglaze enamels of the leaves are subtly used to compliment the brilliance of the flowers. The design itself, while admirably fitted to the size and form of the dish, is tastefully within the informal mode of classic flowering arranging. The back of the dish is decorated with three designs of ribboned cash, and the comb design appears on the foot.

122

FOOTED DISH

Underglaze blue and overglaze enamels
Nabeshima ware, 1st half 18th century
Diameter: 14.9 cm. Height: 4.4 cm. Foot: 8.2 cm.
Mrs. George H. Bunting, Jr.

The Nabeshima artisans seem to have been particularly successful with the designs for small dishes using the maple leaf motif. Leaves were used with spider webs, water (See cat. no. 123) and other variations. One of the most interesting, and certainly the most poetic, examples of this motif is Mrs. Bunting's plate. Here the scheme presents a view of the moon through maple leaves and branches. This interesting theme is achieved by leaving the center of the dish a pure white from which ever-darkening washes of underglaze blue proceed to the edges. A reticulated pattern of branches in white reserve surround the outside of the dish. Underglaze blue, green, red and yellow maple leaves are superimposed on and intertwined among the branches. The back is decorated with three designs of four ribboned cash. These designs and the comb design on the foot are carefully drawn and washed,

123

FOOTED DISH

Underglaze blue and overglaze enamels
Nabeshima ware, 1st half 18th century
Diameter: 15.0 cm. Height: 4.5 cm. Foot: 8.4 cm.
Mr. and Mrs. Henry Trubner

The Japanese appreciation for the beauty of autumn maple leaves is seen here again in this design of leaves and water. Some of the leaves are seen falling or floating, and others are partially submerged in the eddies. Each leaf is carefully outlined in a rich iron red, augmented by either a soft blue-green, pale yellow or completely washed by the iron red itself. The underglaze blue is pale and carefully washed. The back of the plate is decorated with three designs of four ribboned cash, and the foot has a finely painted comb pattern. The underglaze blue on the back is considerably darker than that on the front.

124

FOOTED DISH

Underglaze blue and overglaze enamels
Nabeshima ware, 1st half 18th century
Diameter: 14.8 cm. Height: 4.2 cm. Foot: 8.0 cm.
Mrs. George H. Bunting, Jr.

The design scheme of this plate would seem to be a naturalistic one in which floral forms are silhouetted against the sea and dunes or other natural formations. The flower forms are referred to as hollyhock in several Japanese publications, but it would appear more likely that they represent plantain lily of the *Hosta plataginea* variety, or *tomano-kangashi* in Japanese. The flower heads are painted in a rich red outline and the leaves are painted in underglaze blue with the addition of blue, green and yellow. The back of the plate has the four cash ribboned and comb design on the foot in finely painted underglaze blue.

125

TWO SMALL, FOOTED DISHES
Underglaze blue and overglaze enamels
Nabeshima ware, early 18th century
Diameter: 14.8 cm. Height: 4.2 cm. Foot: 8.0 cm.
City Art Museum of Saint Louis,
W. K. Bixby Oriental Art Trust Fund
12:61.1 and .2

The design is presumably that of wild rose vines.
The back is decorated with three designs of four
ribboned cash and the comb pattern is applied
to the foot rim. The interior decoration is painted
in a dark iron red, blue-green and pale yellow.
The underglaze blue is sparsely used as a wash
in some of the leaves and in the heart of the
flowers. The green and yellow enamels degrade
the surrounding surface of the glaze. The underglaze blue decoration on the back is darker than
that on the front and penetrates the surface of
the glaze in some of the drawing. A dish of
identical design but totally different coloring may
be seen in *Iro Nabeshima,* (See ref. 27, color pl. 64).
Sister Johanna Becker has published a plate
which is probably from the same set as City Art
Museum's.

126

DISH WITH CELADON RIM
Floral and fretwork decoration
in underglaze blue
Nabeshima ware, 18th century
Diameter: 15.4 cm. Height: 4.4 cm. Foot: 8.0 cm.
Mr. and Mrs. John A. Pope

This dish is formed very much as are the more
common rimless vessels, except that the upper
walls of the dish are thicker in order to support
the flattened rim. The thick celadon glaze on
the rim is a simple and effective device that
adds considerable warmth to the blue and white
decoration in addition to giving the form a
greater appearance of solidity and depth. The
ji-i type cartouches and medallions are carefully
positioned for perfect balance against the white
background and the blue segment with fine fretwork patterning. The back of the dish is decorated with three ribboned single cash designs.

Comb pattern appears on the foot. The underglaze blue on the back is clean and rich but
much darker than on the interior.

127

FOOTED DISH
Underglaze blue and overglaze enamels
Nabeshima ware, 1st half 18th century
Diameter: 20.6 cm. Height: 5.8 cm. Foot: 11.0 cm.
City Art Museum of Saint Louis
2:62

The design motif here is of camellias threaded
together in the manner of the Hawaiian lei. The
three strings of flowers are arranged around the
outer edges of the plate leaving a generous, open,
central space. The color scheme is as subdued
as the design, with an extensive use of underglaze blue, pale yellow and shaded washes of
iron red. The back is decorated with three groups
of ribboned six cash designs. These and the comb
pattern on the high foot are meticulously drawn
and painted with light underglaze blue washes.
The yellow enamel is somewhat ochre hued and
crackled where thick, only slightly degrading the
surrounding glaze. The glaze has a slight, but
marked, greenish cast.

128

FOOTED DISH
Underglaze blue and overglaze enamels
Nabeshima ware, 1st half 18th century
Diameter: 19.9 cm. Height: 5.3 cm. Foot: 11.0 cm.
Nelson Gallery—Atkins Museum
63.6

Large size dishes of comparatively early date are
difficult to come by in American collections.
This particularly beautiful example is decorated
with a design of peonies and wave pattern. The
drawing of the underglaze blue is carefully and
competently done, and the shading is meticulously carried out. This same concern for technical perfection is seen in the drawing and
application of the overglaze enamels. The design scheme itself is most interesting. The naturalistic floral forms in combination with the

stylized wave pattern which divide the dish are so arranged as to give a sense of three dimensionality to the design. The back of the dish is decorated with three designs of ribboned four cash motives. The high foot is decorated with comb pattern. The underglaze blue is finely painted and darker than that on the inside of the dish.

129
FOOTED DISH
Underglaze blue with celadon glaze
Nabeshima ware, 18th century
Diameter: 11.6 cm. Height: 3.2 cm. Foot: 6.2 cm.
Honolulu Academy of Arts
3666.1

This beautiful little dish is decorated on the inside with a theme of autumn grasses in underglaze blue under a celadon glaze. The design is simply drawn in single, bending lines with only the translation of the artist's perception of the growing form of grasses and four spikelets to convey the theme. The very thick celadon glaze compliments the underglaze blue, which, in turn, takes on a deep greyed blue hue from the thickness and color of the glaze. The exterior and base are also thickly covered with an undecorated celadon glaze. The thin lip rim is of a paler green caused by the thinness of the glaze at the edge. A small gold lacquer repair is visible on the rim.

130
FOOTED DISH
Underglaze blue with celadon glaze
Nabeshima ware, 18th century
Diameter: 20.2 cm. Height: 5.4 cm. Foot: 10.4 cm.
Nelson Gallery—Atkins Museum,
Gift of Mrs. George H. Bunting, Jr.
68-49/4

The striking design of bamboo leaves is painted in a vivid, dark underglaze blue beneath a very thick, bluish-green celadon glaze. The entire dish, with the exception of the bottom of the foot rim, is covered by the thick glaze. The ex-

terior is undecorated. The potting is very thick, except as it tapers to the fine rim and in the foot. The foot is quite high (2.0 cm.) and straight. Great care was taken in the drawing of the bamboo leaves on the curving surfaces of the dish so that the strong design is not distorted by the shape. While this piece is difficult to date accurately, it is presumed that it was made within the first half of the 18th century.

131
DISH
Underglaze blue and celadon
Nabeshima ware, 18th century
Diameter: 20.0 cm. Height: 5.8 cm. Foot: 10.9 cm.
The Metropolitan Museum of Art,
Gift of Mrs. V. Everit Macy, 1923
23.225.309

Although this dish appears to be a little later than the other dishes of this size in the exhibition, it shows by the quality of its design and execution that the later wares were not universally debased in quality. The body is well formed and the porcelain is fine and white. The glaze is quite white by comparison with early 18th century pieces. Two curving, intersecting geometric repeats form the basis of the design. In some of the Nabeshima literature these forms are referred to as being associated with tents, but this connection is unclear. The three segments so formed by the motif are decorated with *sei-gai-ha,* or repeating wave pattern, a beautiful, clear celadon and the pure white of the undecorated glaze. The reverse is decorated with three designs of peony flower with central cash and leafy scrolling.

132
FOOTED DISH
Wave design in underglaze blue
Nabeshima ware, late 18th–early 19th century
Diameter: 20.4 cm. Height: 5.7 cm. Foot: 11.3 cm.
The Dayton Art Institute,
Gift of Mrs. Eugene W. Kettering
69.420

Much of the later Nabeshima ware was decorated in poorly done repetitions of the early styles.

There were produced, however, original and vigorous designs such as this example. The design is well suited to the shape of the dish and is painted in a robust manner in good underglaze blue. The back is decorated with three designs of peony flowers with leaves. The foot carries the traditional comb pattern. The whiteness of the ware and the quality of the decoration on the back and foot would indicate a fairly late date for the piece.

133
FOOTED DISH
Willow in mists in underglaze blue
Nabeshima ware, 1st half 18th century
Diameter: 30.5 cm. Height: 7.5 cm. Foot: 14.9 cm.
The Cleveland Museum of Art,
Gift of the Twentieth Century Club
62.261

This is the largest Nabeshima dish in the exhibition and is the largest ware usually made by the kiln. Among the round-footed dishes, it is referred to as the *shaku* size—about a foot in diameter. The design concept employed in the decoration is masterful. The strong vertical and horizontal elements provide solidity and formal balance which is relieved by the circular curve of the tree trunk and the delicate descending forms of the willow leaves and branches. The careful shading of the underglaze blue and the excellent, sensitive rendering of the willow leaves contribute directly to the design scheme as well as to its theme. The back of the plate is decorated with the comb pattern on the foot and three designs of four cash with complex arrangements of wide ribbons. These motives are carefully drawn and meticulously shaded. These rather baroque designs are the prototype of the heavy and clumsy decoration found on the backs of so many large 19th century dishes. A smaller dish with a simpler design of willows in mists may be seen in *Iro Nabeshima* (See ref. 27, pl. 35).

134
FOLIATED DISH
Herons in water in underglaze blue
Arita ware, Matsugatani type
Late 17th century
Length: 16.9 cm. Height: 1.2 cm.
City Art Museum of Saint Louis,
W. K. Bixby Oriental Art Trust Fund
114:69

This delicately molded and painted dish has a superbly conceived design of herons surrounded by water and waves drawn in a dark underglaze blue with pale, well modulated washes in lighter blue. There is great strength and vitality in the composition despite the delicacy of some of the rendering and potting. Unlike most pottery decoration, where the skill of the painter is in his ability to fit the design to the vessel, this piece was designed as a whole. The interdependency of molded form and underglaze painting is seen in the re-echoing of the wave designs in the curving lip and in the molded wave forms reinforced by the most subtle shading in underglaze blue. Although in a totally different vein, the exterior decoration is no less inventive in its conception. With great economy the painter has achieved what amounts to two miniature landscape scenes of mountains in mists in the narrow confines of the under rim.

135
SMALL FOLIATE DISH
Underglaze blue and overglaze enamels
Arita ware, Matsugatani type
1st half 18th century
Length: 16.2 cm. Height: 2.8 cm.
Eugene Fuller Memorial Collection,
Seattle Art Museum
65.J27.70

Rarely does one find underglaze blue and overglaze enamels used in such a striking and original manner as in this small molded dish. The central molded design is shaded with underglaze blue; the rest of the dish is painted with black, reserving the molded designs for the brilliant green enamel on the leaves, aubergine for the scrolling and yellow for the decorative dots on the scrolling. The technique is that used for the Ao-Kutani wares but with an entirely different intent. The back is undecorated and the rather thin glaze has gone somewhat matte in one of the firings. The piece rests on a high, oval, sturdy foot which shows the paste to be very fine grained and white. Another example which is probably from the same set is in the Avery Brundage Collection in San Francisco.

136
COVERED JAR
Landscape design in underglaze blue
Hirado ware, 19th century
Height: 21.7 cm. Diameter: 20.4 cm. Foot: 13.0 cm.
Mr. and Mrs. John A. Pope

In terms of technical excellence and delicacy of decoration, the Hirado wares must be considered the finest of later Japanese porcelain. Unfortunately, the majority of these wares found in Western collections are of rather late vintage and are little more than tasteless exercises in ceramic virtuosity. The excellence of the technical qualities of the body and glaze must, however, be admired for their own sake, especially when ennobled by the superior decorative treatment we find here. The landscape is painted most competently and shows both vigor and sensitivity. The modeling of the crouching rabbit finial and the lion masks is cleanly and simply stated in the manner of the best of Chinese blanc-de-Chîne from Tê-hua. Both the underglaze blue and this modeled decoration "fit" the body well. While the landscape decoration has absolutely nothing to do with the modeled forms, the two decorative themes are not in conflict with one another, and indeed are strangely compatible. While these wares have not found much favor in the West among connoisseurs and collectors, this attitude will probably change as objects of finer quality are seen and as we begin to better understand the culture of Japan in the late Edo period.

Bibliographic References

1. Becker, Sister Johanna. "A Group of Nabeshima Porcelain," *The University of Michigan Museum of Art Bulletin,* Vol. III, 1968, pp. 18-28.

2. Ceramic Society of Japan (ed.). *Tosetsu,* January, 1966,

3. Fedderson, Martin. *Japanese Decorative Art.* Translated by Katherine Watson. New York: Thomas Yoseloff, 1962.

4. Frank, Ann. *Chinese Blue and White.* New York: Walker and Company, 1969.

5. Gerry, Roger and Butler, Joseph T. "Japanese Export Porcelain for the American Market," *Antiques Magazine,* Vol. 95, No. 4 (April, 1969), pp. 544-546.

6. Hannover, Emil. *Pottery and Porcelain, A Handbook for Collectors, Vol. II. The Far East.* New York: Scribner's, 1925.

7. Hayashita, Seizo. *Artistic Development of Japanese Ceramics.* Introductory material translated by Kaneko Shigeta. Tokyo: Kawade Publishing Co., 1960.

8. Heinrich, Theodore Allen. *Art Treasures in the Royal Ontario Museum.* Toronto: McClelland and Stewart, Ltd., 1963.

9. Hobson, R. L. *Handbook of Pottery and Porcelain of the Far East in the British Museum.* London, 1924.

10. Honey, William Bower. *The Ceramic Art of China and Other Countries of the Far East.* London: Faber and Faber Limited and the Hyperion Press Limited, 1945.

11. *Japanese Art in the Seattle Art Museum.* Seattle Art Museum, 1960.

12. Jenyns, Soame. "The Chinese Ko-Sometsuke and Shonsui Wares," *Transactions of the Oriental Ceramic Society, 1962-1963,* Vol. 34. London: 1964, pp. 13-50.

13._____. "The Chinese Porcelains in the Topkapu Saray, Instanbul." *Transactions of the Oriental Ceramic Society, 1964-1966,* Vol. 36. London: 1967, pp. 43-72.

14._____. *Japanese Porcelain.* New York: Frederick A. Praeger, 1965.

15. Koyama, Fujio (ed.). *Japanese Ceramics from Ancient to Modern Times.* Oakland Art Museum, 1961.

16. Lane, Arthur. *Later Islamic Pottery.* London: Faber and Faber Limited, 1954.

17. Lee, Sherman E. *A History of Far Eastern Art:* New York: Harry N. Abrams, Inc., 1964.

18._____. "Japanese Art at Seattle," *Oriental Art,* Vol. II, No. 2 (Winter, 1949-1950), pp. 89-98.

19._____. *The Japanese Decorative Style.* Cleveland: The Cleveland Museum of Art, 1961.

20. Lerner, Martin. "Tea-Ceremony Pottery and Export Porcelain," *The Bulletin of the Cleveland Museum of Art,* Vol. LIV, No. 9 (November, 1967).

21. *Masterpieces of Japanese Art.* Dallas: Dallas Museum of Fine Arts, 1969.

22. Mayuyama, Junkichi. *Japanese Art in the West.* Tokyo: Mayuyama and Company, 1966.

23. Mikami, Tsugio. *Toki (Japanese Ceramics).* Tokyo: 1968.

24. Miller, Roy Andrew. *Japanese Ceramics.* After the Japanese text by Seichi Okuda, Fujito Koyama, and Seizo Hayashita. Tokyo: Toto Shuppan Co., Ltd., 1960.

25. Mitzuoka, Tadanari. *Ceramic Art of Japan.* Tokyo: Japan Travel Bureau, 1954.

26. Munsterberg, Hugo. *Art of the Far East.* New York: Harry N. Abrams, Inc., 1968.

27. Nabeshima House Factory Research Committee. *Iro Nabeshima (Nabeshima Colored Porcelains).* Kyoto: Heian-do, 1954.

28. Noma, Seiroku. *The Arts of Japan, Late Medieval to Modern.* Translated and adapted by Glenn T. Webb. Vol. II, Tokyo and Palo Alto: Kodansha International, Ltd., 1967.

29. Okuda, Seiichi. Koyama, Fujio and Hayashita, Seizo. *Japanese Ceramics.* Tokyo: Toto Bunka Co., 1954.

30. Old Imari Research Committee (ed.). *Ko-Imari (Old Imari).* Tokyo: Saga: Kinkado, 1959.

31. *Oriental Art in America, Recent Accessions in American Museums.* Chicago: The New Orient Society of America, 1937.

32. Sansom, George Bailey. *A History of Japan, 1615-1667,* Vol. III. Stanford: Stanford University Press, 1963.

33. Schöbel, Heinz. *"The Four Dimensions of Avery Brundage, Leipzig, 1968,"* Tosetsu. January, 1968.

34. *Sekai toji zenshu (Catalogue of the World's Ceramics),* Vols. IV-VII, Tokyo: Zauho Press & Kawade Shobo, 1955-56.

35. Sera, Yosuke (ed.). *Ko-Imari Sometsuke Zufu (Old Imari, Blue and White Porcelain).* Kyoto: Heian-do, 1959.

36. Syz, Hans. "Some Oriental Aspects of European Ceramic Decoration," *Antiques Magazine,* Vol. 95, No. 5 (May, 1969), pp. 670-681.

37. The Brooklyn Museum. *Japanese Ceramics from the Collection of Captain and Mrs. Roger Gerry,* 1961.

38. *Toki Zenshu (Ceramic Series).* 24 Vols. Tokyo: Heibonsha Ltd., 1957-1960.

39. Volker, T. *The Japanese Porcelain Trade of the Dutch East India Company after 1683.* Leiden: E. J. Brill, 1959.

40._____. *Porcelain and the Dutch East India Company As Recorded in the Dagh-Registers of Batavia Castle, Those of Hirado and Deshima and Other Contemporary Papers, 1602-1682.* Leiden: E. J. Brill, 1954.

41. Yamane, Yuzu. *Nihon Iroe Kotoshu (Japanese Colored Porcelain).* Kyoto: Kyoto-Shoin, 1953.